ANTONIO VIVALDI

LE QUATTRO STAGIONI
THE FOUR SEASONS

Concertos for Violin, Strings and Basso continuo
Op. 8/1–4
(RV 269, 315, 293, 2

Edited by
Simon Launchbur

Ernst Eulenburg Ltd
London · Mainz · Madrid · New York · Paris · Prague · Tokyo · Toronto · Zürich

Performing material based on this edition is available from the publisher /
Der hier veröffentlichte Notentext ist auch als Aufführungsmaterial beim Verlag erhältlich /
Le matériel d'exécution réalisé à partir de cette édition est disponible auprès de l'éditeur

Eulenburg Orchestral Series
EOS 1220, 1221, 1222, 1223

Ernst Eulenburg Ltd
48 Great Marlborough Street
London W1F 7BB

CONTENTS

PREFACE

The *Four Seasons* are the first four of twelve concertos published as the *opera ottava* of Vivaldi by Le Cene of Amsterdam c.1725 with the title: 'Il Cimento dell'Armonia e dell'Invenzione' ('The Contest of Harmony and Invention'). Vivaldi added titles to several of his works, as was fashionable at the time, but the *Four Seasons* are unique in that they are prefaced by descriptive sonnets, assumed to be by the composer himself, which, as he writes in the dedicatory epistle, '[...] explain the music more easily'. The sections of the sonnets were initialled and the phrases inserted in the instrumental parts at the appropriate place. As well as the sonnets themselves, Vivaldi also added narrative captions to certain passages to highlight the descriptive nature of the music. This text matter is set out in a conflicting and generally haphazard manner in the source and a certain amount of tacit editorial adjustment has been made in the present edition particularly concerning the consistency of spelling and capitalization.

As there is no extant autograph the present edition is based on a copy of the early edition by Le Cene, now in the British Library, London (detailed in the Textual Notes below). This source contains many phrasing and dynamic markings, and any editorial additions are for the sake of conformity between identical sections and unanimity between the parts; these are indicated within square brackets or in the case of slurs and ties as broken ligatures. The notational distinction of the two forms of staccato marking found in the source (i.e., the stroke and the dot) has been retained in this edition. Where a tempo indication appears with a dynamic mark in the source, e.g., *p e larghetto*, the tempo mark is placed above the system and the dynamic marking below in this edition.

The term *Organo* in the instrumental bass section is taken to mean an appropriate keyboard instrument, most certainly a harpsichord in the present context. The indication *Tasto solo* (without harmonization) is only occasionally terminated with a *Tutti* marking in the source; other necessary *Tutti* markings have been supplied editorially.

The Italian commentary – based on the prefatory sonnets – contains some minor inconsistencies of spelling, capitalization, punctuation, etc., in the sources. These texts have not been modernized in this edition, neither have they been detailed in the Textual Notes.

Simon Launchbury

VORWORT

Die *Vier Jahreszeiten* sind die ersten der zwölf als op. 8 (*opera ottava*) erschienenen Konzerte von Vivaldi, die um 1725 von Le Cene in Amsterdam unter dem Titel *Il Cimento ell'Armonia e dell'Invenzione* („Der Wettstreit zwischen Harmonie und Einfall") herausgegeben wurden. Der damaligen Mode entsprechend hat Vivaldi mehreren seiner Werke einen Titel gegeben; die *Vier Jahreszeiten* sind jedoch insofern einzigartig, als ihnen Sonette vorangestellt sind, die vermutlich vom Komponisten selbst stammen und über die er in seinem Widmungsschreiben äußert, sie „sollten die Musik verständlicher machen". Den einzelnen Abschnitten der Sonette sind Großbuchstaben vorangestellt, und die Worte der Sonette stehen in den Stimmen an entsprechender Stelle. Vivaldi hat neben den Sonetten zudem beschreibende Oberschriften für bestimmte Passagen eingefügt, um den deskriptiven Charakter der Musik herauszustellen. Dieser Aspekt des Textanteils in den *Vier Jahreszeiten* stellt sich in der Quelle (also der Erstausgabe) auf widersprüchliche und durchweg zufällige Art und Weise dar; so hat der Herausgeber dieser Ausgabe prinzipiell bestimmte Berichtigungen besonders im Hinblick auf Übereinstimmung von Wortlaut und den erwähnten Großbuchstaben stillschweigend vorgenommen.

Das Autograph ist nicht erhalten, weshalb diese Ausgabe auf einem Exemplar der Erstausgabe von Le Cene beruht. Es ist heute im Besitz der British Library, London, und wird in den Einzelanmerkungen näher beschrieben. Diese Quelle enthält viele Eintragungen für Phrasierungen und Dynamik. Herausgeberzusätze stellen die Übereinstimmung identischer Stellen und der Stimmen untereinander sicher. Man erkennt sie an eckigen Klammem oder gestrichelten Phrasierungsbögen. Keil und Punkt staccato Vorschrift sind in dieser Ausgabe gemäß der Quelle beibehalten. Bei Tempo Angaben mit dem Zusatz einer dynamischen Vorschrift, beispielsweise *p e larghetto* steht in dieser Ausgabe die Vorschrift für das Tempo über dem System für die Dynamik darunter.

Mit *Organo* in der Bassgruppe ist ein geeignetes Tasteninstrument gemeint, hier mit großer Wahrscheinlichkeit ein Cembalo. Am Ende einer *Tasto solo*-Passage (also ohne Harmonisierung) steht in der Quelle nicht immer *Tutti*. Diese und weitere *Tutti*-Vorschriften hat der Herausgeber hinzugesetzt.

Der italienische Kommentar auf der Grundlage der vorangestellten Sonette enthält in den Quellen, einige unbedeutende Widersprüche in Schreibweise, Großschreibung, Zeichensetzung usw. In dieser Ausgabe wurden diese Texte modernisiert, in den Einzelanmerkungen jedoch nicht näher erklärt.

Simon Launchbury
Übersetzung: Norbert Henning

PRÉFACE

Les *Quatre saisons* sont les quatre premiers de douze concertos publiés comme *opera ottava* de Vivaldi par Le Cene, à Amsterdam, vers 1725, sous le titre de «Il Cimento dell'Armonia e dell'Invenzione» («Le combat de l'Harmonie et de l'Invention»). Selon l'usage en faveur à son époque, Vivaldi ajouta des titres à plusieurs de ses œuvres mais les *Quatres saisons* représentent un cas exceptionnel à cet égard car elles sont précédées de sonnets descriptifs, sans doute écrits par le compositeur lui-même, qui, ainsi qu'il le précise dans sa dédicace, «[...] expliquent plus facilement la musique.» Aux différentes sections des sonnets furent attribuées des lettres et les vers furent insérés dans la partition aux endroits correspondants. En plus des sonnets, Vivaldi illustra quelques passages de légendes narratives qui soulignent la nature descriptive de ces concertos. Ces textes sont généralement placés de façon indécise et fortuite dans la source. Un certain nombre de corrections tacites ont donc été effectuées dans cette édition, notamment en ce qui concerne la cohérence de l'orthographe et des majuscules.

Comme il n'existe aucun manuscrit autographe des œuvres, notre édition s'appuie sur un exemplaire de la première édition de Le Cene conservé à la British Library de Londres (et analysé dans l'appareil critique ci-dessous). Cette source comporte de nombreuses indications de phrasé et de nuances dynamiques; les précisions éditoriales complémentaires ont pour objectif de rétablir la conformité entre sections identiques et la similarité des parties. Celles-ci sont placées entre crochets ou, dans le cas des liaisons et liaisons de phrasés, en pointillé. Les deux formes distinctes de notation du *staccato* figurant dans la source (tiret et point) ont été maintenues. Lorsque dans la source apparaît une indication de tempo accompagnée d'une nuance dynamique, par exemple *p e larghetto*, l'indication de tempo est placée audessus du système et l'indication dynamique en dessous.

Le terme *Organo* à la basse instrumentale désigne tout instrument à clavier approprié, et sûrement le clavecin dans ce contexte. La mention *Tasto solo* (sans harmonisation) n'est que rarement suivie de la notation de reprise du *Tutti* dans la source. Certaines indications de *Tutti* supplémentaires ont été rétablies à l'édition.

Le commentaire en italien – reposant sur les sonnets d'introduction – présente certaines incohérences mineures dans les sources quant à l'orthographe, les majuscules, la ponctuation, etc. Ces textes n'ont pas été modernisés pour cette édition, ni ne font l'objet d'une analyse dans l'appareil critique.

Simon Launchbury
Traduction : Agnès Ausseur

Sonetto Dimostrativo
Sopra il Concerto Intitolato La
PRIMAVERA
DEL SIG.re D. ANTONIO VIVALDI

A Giunt' è la Primavera e festosetti
B La Salutan gl' Augei con lieto canto,
C E i fonti allo Spirar de' Zeffiretti
Con dolce mormorio Scorrono intanto:

D Vengon' coprendo l'aer di nero amanto
E Lampi, e tuoni ad annuntiarla eletti
E Indi tacendo questi, gl' Augelletti;
Tornan' di nuovo al lor canoro incanto:

F E quindi sul fiorito ameno prato
Al caro mormorio di fronde e piante
Dorme 'l Caprar col fido can' à lato.

G Di pastoral Zampogna al Suon festante
Danzan Ninfe e Pastor nel tetto amato
Di primavera all' apparir brillante.

Sonnets/Sonette/Sonnets

SPRING

A Spring has arrived, and
B the birds cheerfully greet her with joyful song,
C while the streams, at the Zephyrs' gentle blowing,
flow with sweet murmuring.

D The sky becomes cloaked in amarantine black
by the noble heralds of thunder and lightning.
E Then silencing them, the little birds
return to their enchanting song.

F And so, on the pleasant flowery meadow
to the gentle murmur of leaves and plants,
the goatherd sleeps with his faithful dog at his side.

G To the festive sound of country bagpipes,
nymphs and shepherds dance beneath the beloved vault
at the shining appearance of spring.

Translation Peter Owens

FRÜHLING

A Der Frühling ist gekommen, und
B freudig begrüßen ihn die Vögel mit heiterem Gesang,
C und die Ströme fließen mit süßem Murmeln zu den leise
wehenden Zephirwinden dahin.

D Von Donner und Blitz, den Vorboten des Gewitters, wird
der Himmel in ein dunkelrot-schwarzes Gewand gehüllt.
E Zunächst verstummt, trillern die Vögelein dann wieder
ihre bezaubernden Lieder.

F Und auf den lieblichen Blumenwiesen,
beim zarten Rauschen von Blättern und Pflanzen,
schlummern Seite an Seite der Hirte und sein treuer Hund.

G Zu den festlichen Klängen der Dudelsackpfeifer
tanzen Nymphen und Hirten unter dem teuren Himmelszelt.
Strahlend ist der Frühling erschienen.

Übersetzung Esther Dubielzig

LE PRINTEMPS

A Le Printemps est arrivé et dans la liesse
B les oiseaux l'accueillent de leurs chants joyeux,
C tandis que les fontaines sous les doux souffles des Zéphyrs
murmurent délicatement.

D Le ciel s'assombrit de noir amarante
annonçant le tonnerre et les éclairs.
E Puis, les faisant taire, les petits oiseaux
reprennent leurs chansons charmeuses.

F Et, ainsi, dans la jolie prairie fleurie,
au doux bruissement des feuilles et des fleurs,
le chevrier est assoupi, son chien fidèle à côté de lui.

G Au son allègre des cornemuses villageoises
dansent les nymphes et les bergers sous la voûte céleste
à l'éclatante apparition du printemps.

Traduction Agnès Ausseur

2

Sonetto Dimostrativo
Sopra il Concerto Intitolato
L'ESTADE
DEL SIG.re D. ANTONIO VIVALDI

A Sotto dura Staggion dal Sole accesa
Langue L'huom, langue 'l gregge, ed arde il Pino;
B Scioglie il Cucco la Voce, e tosto intesa
C Canta la Tortorella e'l gardelino.

D Zeffiro dolce Spira, mà contesa
Muove Borea improviso al Suo vicino;
E E piange il Pastorel, perche Sospesa
Teme fiera borasca, e'l Suo destino:

F Toglie alle membra lasse il Suo riposo
Il timore de' Lampi, e tuoni fieri
E de mosche, e mosconi il Stuol furioso! /e

G Ah che pur troppo i Suoi timor Son veri
Tuona e fulmina il Ciel e grandinoso
Tronca il capo alle Spiche e a'grani alteri

SUMMER

A Under the harsh weather set ablaze by the sun
man and beast languish, and the pine tree is parched.
B The cuckoo loosens his voice, and soon
C the turtle dove and the goldfinch join him in song.

D Sweet Zephyr blows, but in challenge
Boreas suddenly moves to his side,
E and the shepherd boy cries because he is afraid
of the fierce impending storm, and his fate.

F Rest is denied his weary limbs
by the fear of lightning and violent thunder
and the furious swarm of flies and bluebottles.

G Ah, but sadly his fears are real;
the sky thunders and flashes, and with hail
cuts off the head of corn stalks and of lofty wheat.

Translation Peter Owens

SOMMER

A In der sengenden Glut der Sonne ermatten Mensch und Tier,
und die Pinien verdorren.
B Der Kuckuck erhebt seine Stimme, und bald schon
C fallen Taube und Stieglitz in seinen Gesang mit ein.

D Sacht' weht der Zephir, doch plötzlich stellt sich ihm
herausfordernd der Nordwind zur Seite.
E Der Hirtenjunge schreit auf, voller Angst vor dem
drohenden unbändigen Sturm und vor seinem Schicksal.

F Verwehrt ist seinen müden Gliedern die Ruhe
aus Angst vor Blitz und krachendem Donner
und den wilden Schwärmen von Fliegen und Brummern.

G Ach, seine Befürchtungen sind nur allzu wahr;
vom Himmel ertönt Donner, leuchten Blitze,
und Hagelschauer verwüsten die wogenden Getreidefelder.

Übersetzung Esther Dubielzig

L'ÉTÉ

A Pendant les jours torrides enflammés de soleil
l'homme et la bête reposent et le pin se dessèche.
B Le coucou élève la voix et bientôt
C la tourterelle et le chardonneret se joignent à lui.

D Le doux Zéphyr souffle mais, le défiant,
Boréas soudain l'accompagne,
E et le berger pleure de peur
face à l'orage terrible qui menace et face à son destin.

F Point de repos pour ses membres fatigués
devant la crainte de l'éclair et du violent tonnerre,
et de la nuée furieuse des mouches.

G Ah! Que sa crainte est juste,
le ciel gronde et s'embrase et la grêle
tranche les épis de maïs.

Traduction Agnès Ausseur

3

Sonetto Dimostrativo
Sopra il Concerto Intitolato
L'AUTUNNO
DEL SIG.^{re} D. ANTONIO VIVALDI

A Celebra il Vilanel con balli e Canti
Del felice raccolto il bel piacere
B E del liquor di Bacco accesi tanti
C Finiscono col Sonno il lor godere

D Fà ch'ogn'uno tralasci e balli e canti
L'aria che temperata dà piacere,
E la Staggion ch'invita tanti e tanti
D'un dolcissimo Sonno al bel godere.

E I cacciator alla nov' alba à caccia
Con corni, Schioppi, e canni escono fuore
F Fugge la belua, e Seguono la traccia;

G Già Sbigottita, e lassa al gran rumore
De' Schioppi e canni, ferita minaccia
H Languida di fuggir, mà oppressa muore

AUTUMN

A The peasant celebrates, with dances and singing,
the great joy of a fortunate harvest;
B and many, inflamed by Bacchus' liquor,
C end their merriment in sleep.

D Everyone is induced to leave the singing and dancing
by the temperate air which brings contentment
and the time which invites so many
to the gentle delight of a sweet sleep.

E The hunters go out to hunt at daybreak
with horns, guns and dogs.
F The wild beast flees, and they follow the trail.

G Already dazed and exhausted by the great clamour
of guns and dogs, wounded, it weakly threatens
H to escape but is overpowered and dies.

Translation Peter Owens

HERBST

A Mit Tanz und Gesang feiern die Bauern
glücklich die gute Ernte;
B viele huldigen ausgiebig dem Bacchus, und
C ihre Fröhlichkeit endet schließlich in süßem Schlummer.

D Die milde Luft, die Zufriedenheit schafft,
und die Zeit, die so viele zu dem schönen Vergnügen
eines süßen Schlummers einlädt,
bringt alle dazu, mit dem Singen und Tanzen aufzuhören.

E Die Jäger begeben sich bei Tagsanbruch auf die Jagd,
mit Hörnern, Gewehren und Hunden.
F Das Wild, es flieht, doch sie folgen seiner Spur.

G Schon benommen und erschöpft vom großen Lärm der Gewehre
H und Hunde, verwundet gar, unternimmt es einen schwachen
Versuch zu entkommen, doch es wird bezwungen und verendet.

Übersetzung Esther Dubielzig

L'AUTOMNE

A Les villageois fêtent en danses et en chansons
la joie de la bonne récolte
B et beaucoup, enfiévrés par la liqueur de Bacchus,
C achèvent les festivités dans le sommeil.

D Tous cessent les danses et les chansons
dans l'air doux qui réjouit
et à l'heure qui invite
aux délices d'un paisible sommeil.

E Le chasseur se met en route au lever du jour
avec les cors, les fusils et les chiens.
F La bête s'enfuit et il suit sa trace.

G Déjà étourdie et épuisée par la forte clameur
des fusils et des chiens, blessée, elle tente faiblement
H de s'échapper mais elle est capturée et meurt.

Traduction Agnès Ausseur

4

Sonetto Dimostrativo

Sopra il Concerto Intitolato

L'INVERNO

DEL SIG.re D. ANTONIO VIVALDI

A Aggiacciato tremar trà nevi algenti
B Al Severo Spirar d'orrido Vento,
C Correr battendo i piedi ogni momento;
D E pel Soverchio gel batter i denti;

E Passar al foco i dì quieti e contenti
Mentre la pioggia fuor bagna ben cento /a
F Caminar Sopra 'l giaccio, e à passo lento
G Per timor di cader girsene intenti; /i

H Gir forte, Sdrucciolar, cader à terra
I Di nuovo ir Sopra 'l giaccio e correr forte
L Sin ch' il giaccio Si rompe, e Si disserra;

M Sentir uscir dalle ferrate porte
N Sirocco, Borea, e tutti i Venti in guerra
Quest' è 'l verno, mà tal, che gioja apporte

WINTER

A Chilled and shivering in the snow which freezes
B at the terrible wind's hard blast;
C running with feet stamping all the time,
D and teeth chattering because of the extreme cold;

E spending peaceful and happy days by the fire
while the rain outside pours down heavily;
F walking on the ice and, with a slow step,
G going carefully around it for fear of falling;

H turning quickly, slipping and falling down;
I going once more on the ice, and running fast
L until the ice cracks and breaks apart;

M hearing, as they come out from the ironclad gates,
N Sirocco, Boreas and all the winds at war:
this is Winter, but what joy it brings.

Translation Peter Owens

WINTER

A Zu frieren und zittern im Schnee, der bei dem
B fürchterlichen Wind gefriert;
C ohne Unterlaß zu laufen, mit den Füßen zu trampeln
D und mit den Zähnen zu klappern wegen der bitteren Kälte.

E Friedliche und frohe Tage am Feuer zu verbringen,
während es draußen in Strömen regnet;
F auf dem Eise zu laufen und es langsamen Schrittes
G und vorsichtig zu überqueren, um nicht zu fallen.

H Schnell zu laufen, auszurutschen und hinzufallen;
I erneut auf's Eis zu gehen und schnell zu rennen,
L bis das Eis kracht und auseinanderbricht.

M Zu hören, wie sie durch die Eisentore hereindrängen,
N der Schirokko, der Nordwind und alle die anderen Winde auf
dem Kriegspfad: Ja, das ist der Winter. Doch welche Freude
er mit sich bringt!

Übersetzung Esther Dubielzig

L'HIVER

A Glacés et frissonnants dans la neige gelée
B sous le vent cruel;
C courir en frappant les pieds sans cesse,
D et en claquant des dents sous le froid extrême;

E passer des jours paisibles et heureux au coin du feu
tandis que la pluie tombe lourdement dehors;
F marcher sur la glace et, d'un pas lent,
G s'en écarter de peur de tomber;

H aller précipitamment, glisser et tomber;
I retourner sur la glace et courir vite
L jusqu'à ce que la glace cède et se brise;

M entendre, à travers les portails de fer,
N Sirocco, Boréas et tous les vents qui luttent:
c'est l'hiver, mais quelles joies il apporte!

Traduction Agnès Ausseur

Textual Notes

IE = First edition, undated c. 1725, in sets of parts, title-page:
IL CIMENTO DELL' ARMONIA/E DELL' INVENTIONE/CONCERTI/a 4 e 5/[...]/DA D. ANTONIO VIVALDI/[...]/OPERA OTTAVA/Libro Primo/A AMSTERDAM/spesà di MICHELE CARLO LE CENE/Librario/No. 520
Set consulted: British Library, London, *GB-Lbl* g.33.c.

n(n) = note(s)
b(b) = bar(s)

Concerto No. 1

Mov. I

bar 46 Vla. 1st beat in IE reads:

Mov. II

10 Vla. nn1, 2 b b in IE

Mov. III

31 Vl. I nn5–6 slurred in IE

Concerto No. 2

Mov. I

25 B.c. IE reads:

49 Vl. II n1 *f* in IE

57 B.c. IE reads:

110 Vla. n1 c in IE

113, 114 Vl. pr. nn1–3 slurred in IE

168 B.c. n2 lacks sharp in IE

Mov. II

19 Vl. II n10 C♯' in IE

Mov. III

16 Vl. pr. n7 hand-written × (= sharp) in IE

113 Vl. I/II n7 ♭ in IE

Concerto No. 3

Mov. I

2 Vl. pr., Vl. I 1E reads: 

14ff Vl. pr. part notated on separate stems in 1E

45 Vl. I/II, B.c. n2 ♭ in 1E

94 Vl. pr. Pia: *p* in 1E

106 Vl. I Allegro molto in 1E

Mov. II

17, 23 Vl. pr. slurs in 1E ; Vl. I slurs in 1E

32–34 Vl. I slurs bb33–34 only in 1E

Mov. III

1 Vl. I *f* in 1E

30ff Vl. pr. part notated on separate stems in 1E

83 Vla. n2 lacks dot in 1E; Vla., B.c. last beat reads in 1E

Concerto No. 4

Mov. II

9 Vl. I n8 b♭′ in 1E

Mov. III

106 Vla. n1 crotchet in 1E

119 Vl. II n2 e♮″ in 1E

CONCERTO No. 1 LA PRIMAVERA

Antonio Vivaldi
(1678–1741)
Op. 8/1
RV 269

Edited by Simon Launchbury

Vl. pr.
I
Vl.
II
Vla.
B. c.
B IL CANTO DE GL'UCELLI
Solo
IL CANTO DE
Solo
IL CANTO DE GL'UCELLI
Solo
GL'AUGELLI

e festosetti la salutan gl'augei con lieto canto,
21
Vl. pr.
I
Vl.
II
tr
23
[tr]
26
Tutti
Vla.
B. c.
6
4
5
3
SCORRONO I FONTI
C e i fonti allo spirar de'zeffiretti
29
p
[p]

con dolce mormorio scorrono intanto:
32
Vl. pr.
I
Vl.
II
Vla.
B. c.
35
Vl. pr.
I
Vl.
II
Vla.
B. c.
6
5
38
Vl. pr.
I
Vl.
II
Vla.
B. c.
f
f
f
[f]
6
5
f

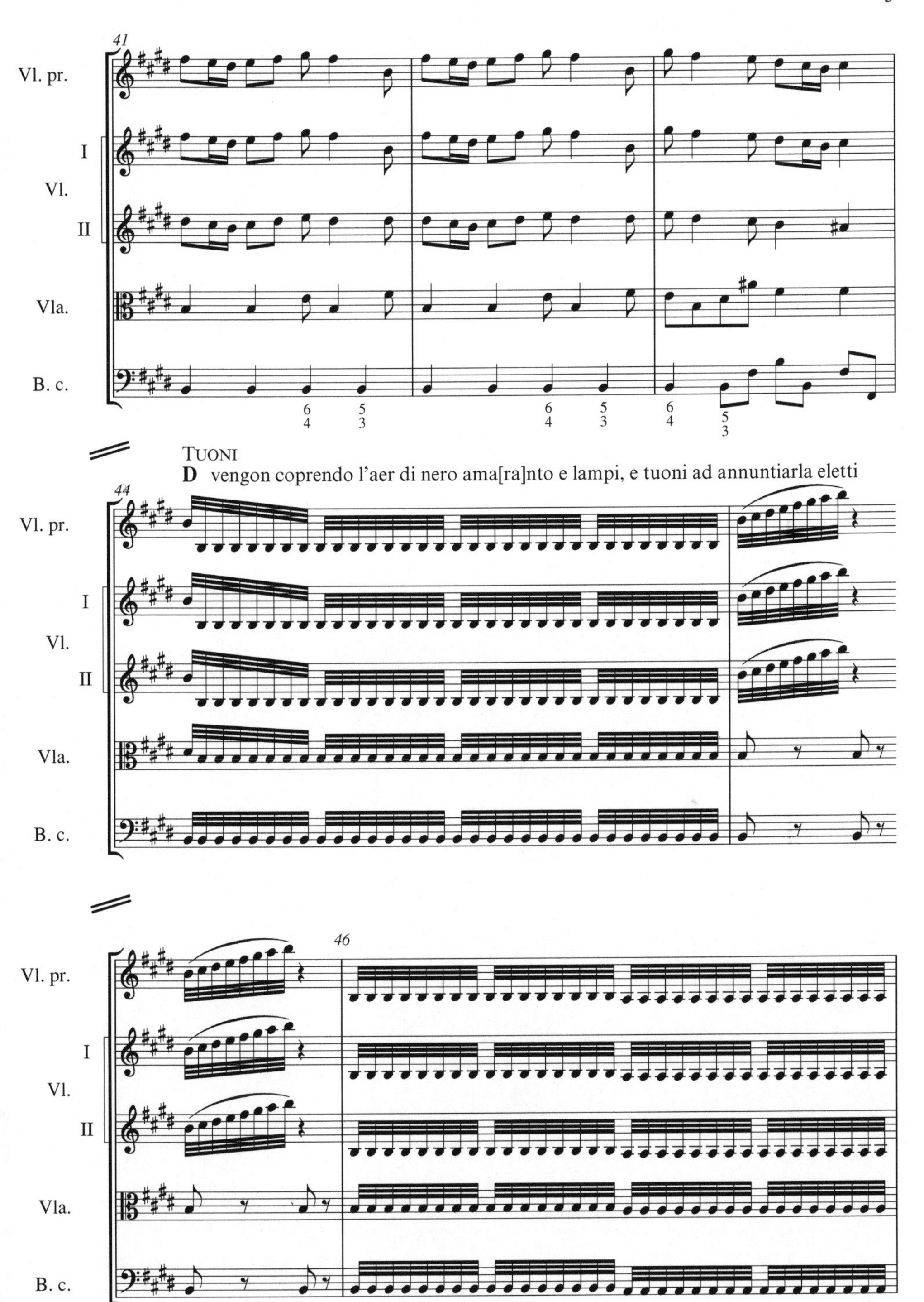
41
Vl. pr.
I
Vl.
II
Vla.
B. c.
6
4
5
3
6
4
5
3
6
4
5
3
TUONI
D vengon coprendo l'aer di nero ama[ra]nto e lampi, e tuoni ad annuntiarla eletti
44
Vl. pr.
I
Vl.
II
Vla.
B. c.
46
Vl. pr.
I
Vl.
II
Vla.
B. c.

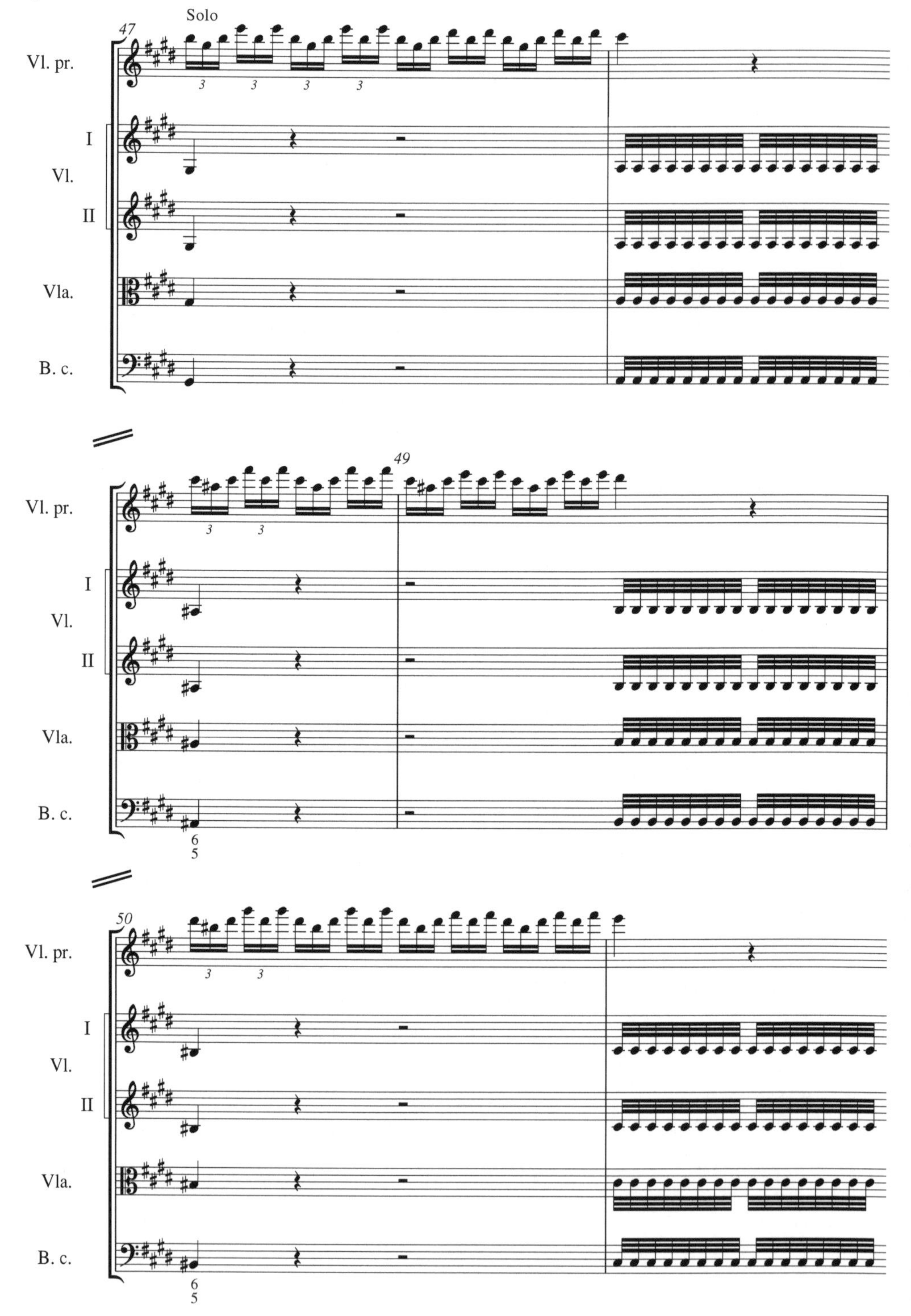
47
Solo
Vl. pr.
I
Vl.
II
Vla.
B. c.
49
Vl. pr.
I
Vl.
II
Vla.
B. c.
6
5
50
Vl. pr.
I
Vl.
II
Vla.
B. c.
6
5

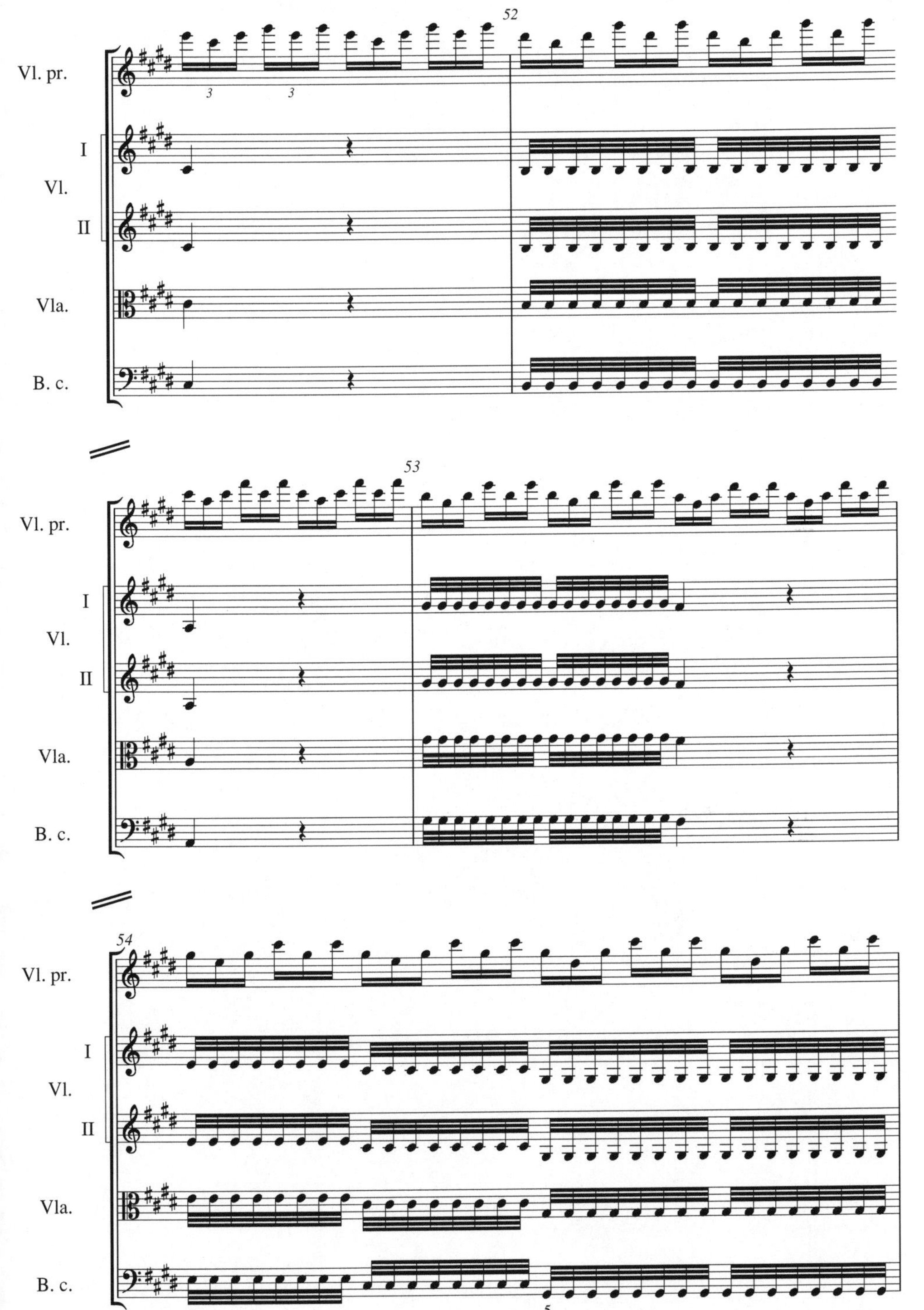
Vl. pr.
I
Vl.
II
Vla.
B. c.
52
53
54
3
3
5
4

55
Vl. pr.
Tutti
I
Vl.
II
Vla.
B. c.
3♯
6 4
5 3
6 4
5 3
Canto d'ucelli
E indi tacendo questi, gl'augeletti; tornan di nuovo al lor
58
Vl. pr.
tr
I
Vl.
II
Vla.
B. c.
Tasto solo
6 4
5 3
canoro incanto:
61
Vl. pr.
tr
Canto d'ucelli
Solo
I
Vl.
II
Canto d'ucelli
Solo
B. c.

64
Vl. pr.
I
Vl.
II
B. c.
66
Tutti
Vla.
7
69
Solo
Tasto solo

72
Vl. pr.
B. c.

75
Vl. pr.
tr
Tutti
tr
I
[tr]
Vl.
II
Vla.
B. c.
[Tutti]
6 5
4 3
6 5
4 3
6 5
4 3

79
Vl. pr.
p
tr
I
p
[tr]
Vl.
II
p
Vla.
p
B. c.
[p]
6 5
4 3
6 5 6 5
4 3 4 3

II. Largo e pianissimo sempre

F E quindi sul fiorito ameno prato al caro mormorio di fronde e piante

si deve suonare sempre molto forte, e strappato

dorme'l caprar col fido can à lato.

11
Vl. pr.
I
Vl.
II
Vla.
14
Vl. pr.
I
Vl.
II
Vla.
17
Vl. pr.
tr
I
Vl.
II
Vla.

Vl. pr.
I
Vl.
II
Vla.

30
Vl. pr.
I
Vl.
II
Vla.
tr
33
Vl. pr.
I
Vl.
II
Vla.
36
Vl. pr.
I
Vl.
II
Vla.
tr

III. Allegro

DANZA PASTORALE

G Di pastoral zampogna al suon festante danzan ninfe e pastor nel tetto

Violino principale

con sordino

I

Violino

con sordino

II

Viola

Organo e Violoncello [Basso continuo]

tr tr

amato di primavera all'apparir brillante.

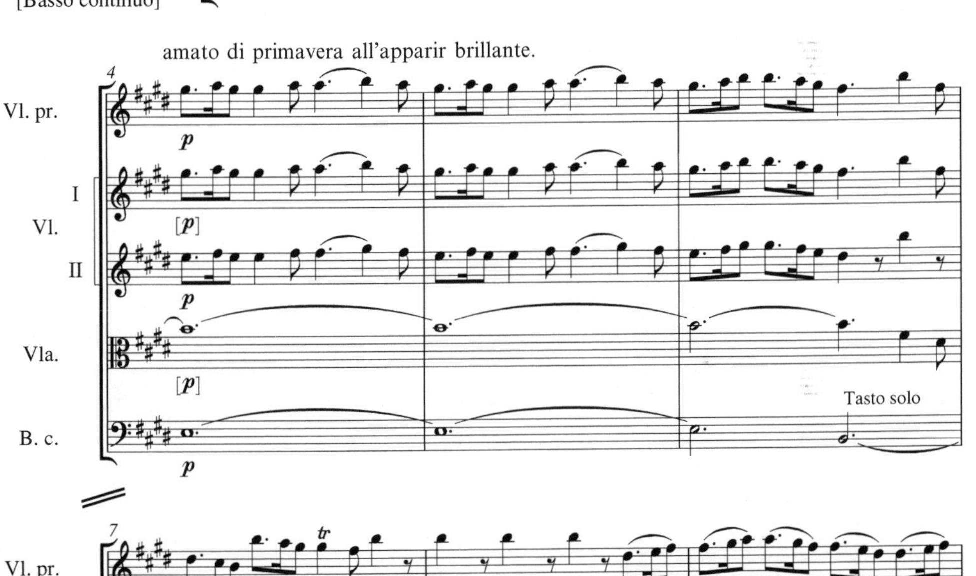

10
Vl. pr.
Solo
I
Vl.
II
Vla.
B. c.
13
Vl. pr.
B. c.
[Tutti]
6
16
Vl. pr.
B. c.
6
6
18
Vl. pr.
B. c.
20
Vl. pr.
Tutti
I
Vl.
II
Vla.
B. c.
Tasto solo
7
5
6
4
5
♯

23
Vl. pr.
I
Vl.
II
Vla.
[Tutti]
B. c.
26
p
29
f

32
Solo
Vl. pr.
I
Vl.
II
Vla.
B. c.
6
4+
2
6
6
5
♯
35
Vl. pr.
Solo
Vl. I
B. c.
37
Vl. pr.
Vl. I
B. c.
6
5♮
7♭
6
5♮
7
39
Vl. pr.
Vl. I
Tasto solo
B. c.
6
5
7

42
Vl. pr.
Vl. I
B. c.
46
Vl. pr.
Tutti
I
Vl.
II
p
p
B. c.
49
Vl. pr.
I
Vl.
II
52
Vl. pr.
I
Vl.
II
Vla.
p

55
Vl. pr.
I
Vl.
II
Vla.
58
Tutti
[f]
f
Tasto solo
B. c.
61
6
4
5
#

Vl. pr.
I
Vl.
II
Vla.
B. c.

Vl. pr.
Solo
I
Vl.
II
Vla.
B. c.
Tasto solo sempre
7 6
Tutti
f
[f]

80
Vl. pr.
I
Vl.
II
Vla.
B. c.
83
Vl. pr.
I
Vl.
II
Vla.
B. c.
86
Vl. pr.
tr
p
[tr]
tr
[p]
p
p
Tutti
Tasto solo
Tutti
[p]

CONCERTO No. 2 L'ESTATE

Antonio Vivaldi
(1678–1741)
Op. 8/2
RV 315

I. Allegro non molto

LANGUIDEZZA PER IL CALDO

A Sotto dura staggion dal sole accesa langue l'huom, langue'l gregge, ed

Violino principale

Violino I

Violino II

Viola

Organo e Violoncello [Basso continuo]

Edited by Simon Launchbury

Vl. pr.
I
Vl.
II
Vla.
B. c.
Allegro e tutto sopra il canto ⋆)
Il cucco
B scioglie il cucco la voce,
sopra il cantino ⋆⋆)
⋆) = sul A
⋆⋆) = sul E

43
Vl. pr.
B. c.
♮ 6
♯ 6
6
6
46
Vl. pr.
B. c.
6
6
6
6
6
♯ 6
49
Tutti
Vl. pr.
I
Vl.
II
Vla.
B. c.
5
4
3♯
52
Solo
Vl. pr.
pp
I
Vl.
pp
II
pp
Vla.
pp
B. c.
pp
6♭

La tortorella
C e tosto intesa canta la tortorella e'l gardelino.
59
Vl. pr.
Tasto solo
B. c.
66
Vl. pr.
I
Vl.
II
Vla.
B. c.
Il gardellino
72
Vl. pr.
I
Vl.
II
Vla.

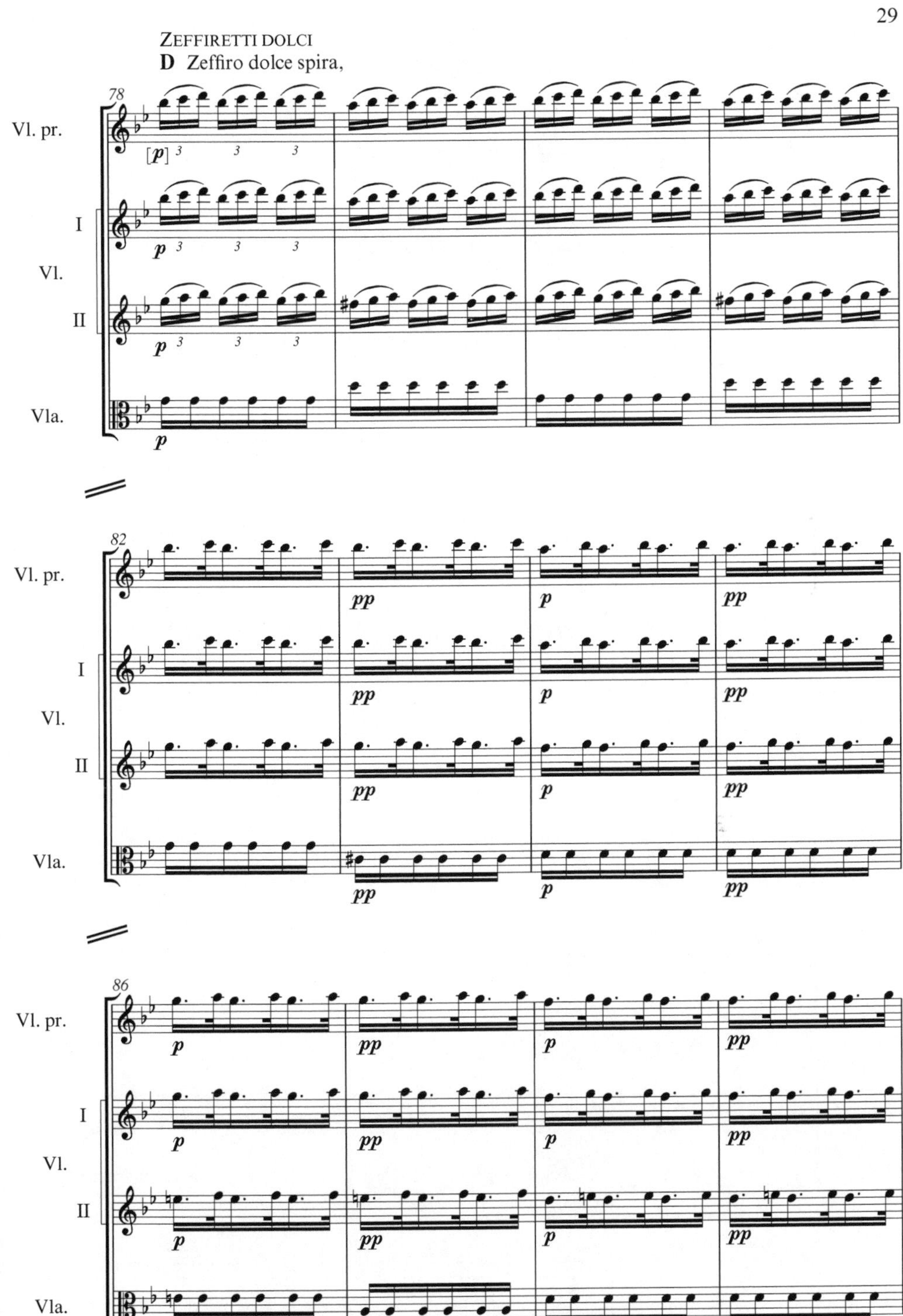
ZEFFIRETTI DOLCI
D Zeffiro dolce spira,
78
Vl. pr.
[p]
I
Vl.
II
Vla.
p
82
pp
86

Vento borea
mà contesa muove Borea improviso al suo vicino;
90
Vl. pr.
f
I
Vl.
f
II
f Venti impettuosi
Vla.
f Venti diversi
B. c.
[f]
6
4
3♯
93
Vl. pr.
I
Vl.
II
Vla.
B. c.
7
5
6
4
97
Vl. pr.
I
Vl.
II
Vla.
B. c.
5
3
8
6
7
5
6
4

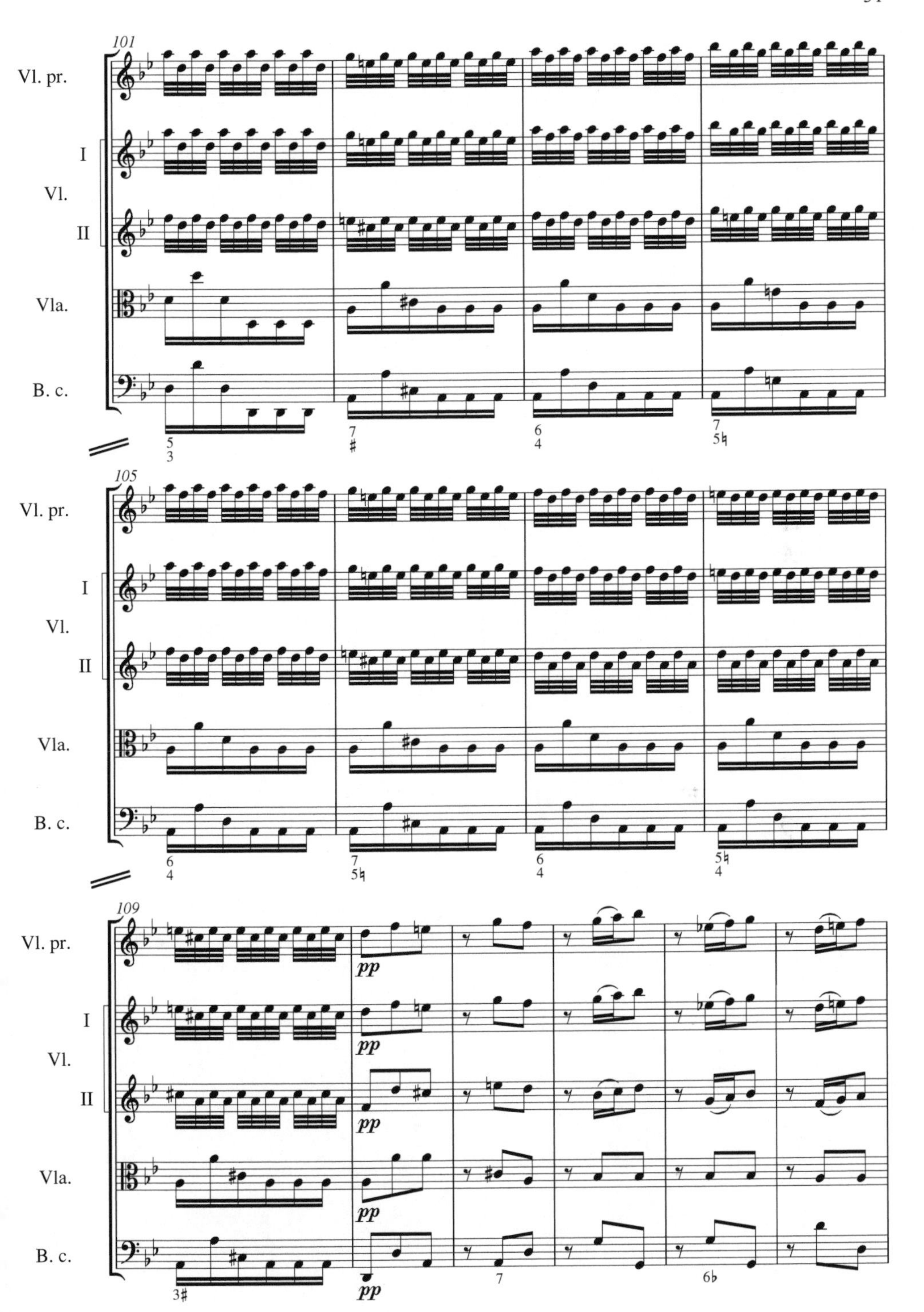
101
Vl. pr.
I
Vl.
II
Vla.
B. c.
5
3
7
♯
6
4
7
5♮
105
Vl. pr.
I
Vl.
II
Vla.
B. c.
6
4
7
5♮
6
4
5♮
4
109
Vl. pr.
pp
I
Vl.
pp
II
pp
Vla.
pp
B. c.
pp
3♯
7
6♭

IL PIANTO DEL VILLANELLO

E e piange il pastorel, perche sospesa teme fiera borasca, e'l suo destino;

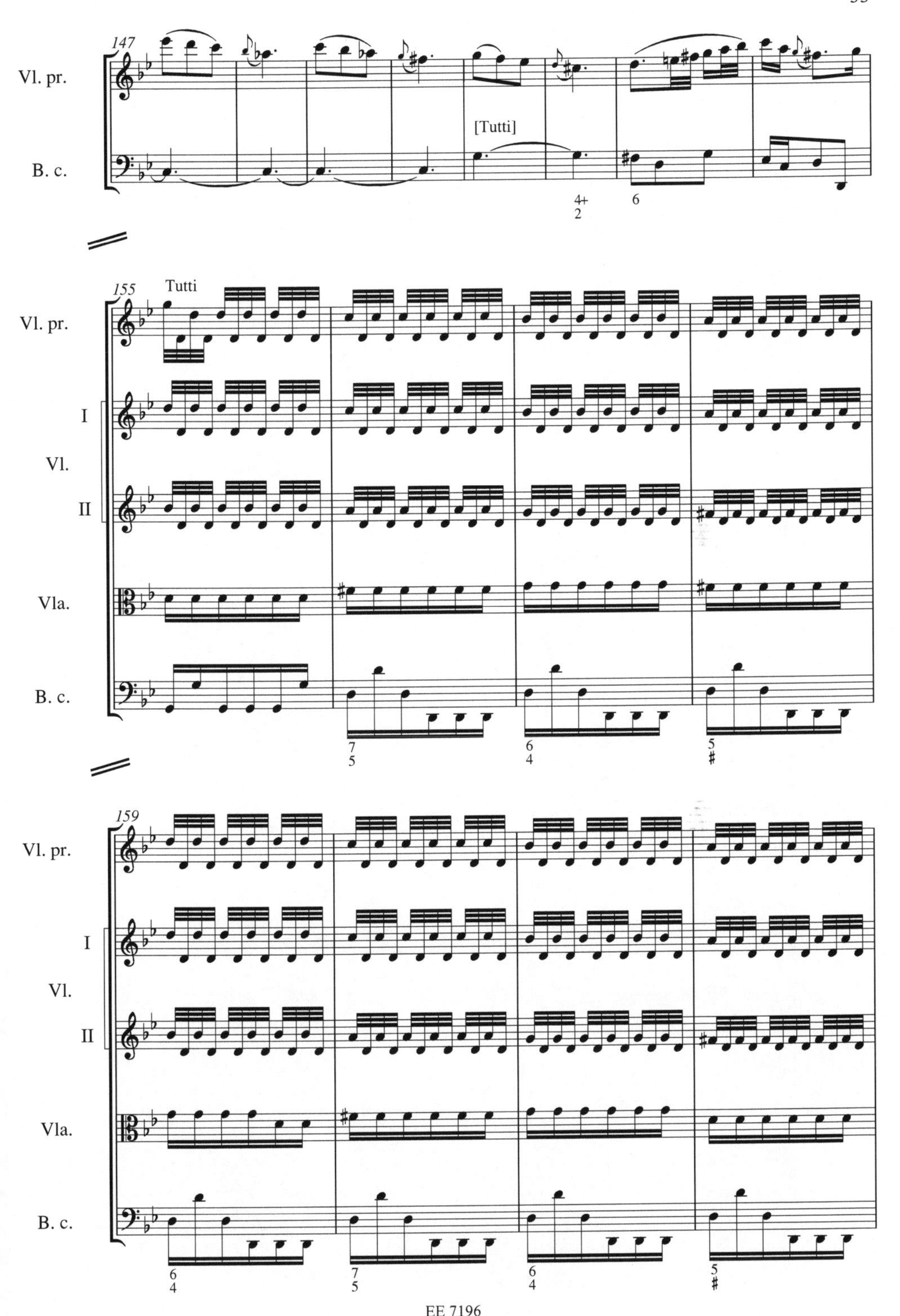
147
Vl. pr.
B. c.
[Tutti]
4+
2
6
155
Tutti
Vl. pr.
I
Vl.
II
Vla.
B. c.
7
5
6
4
5
♯
159
Vl. pr.
I
Vl.
II
Vla.
B. c.
6
4
7
5
6
4
5
♯

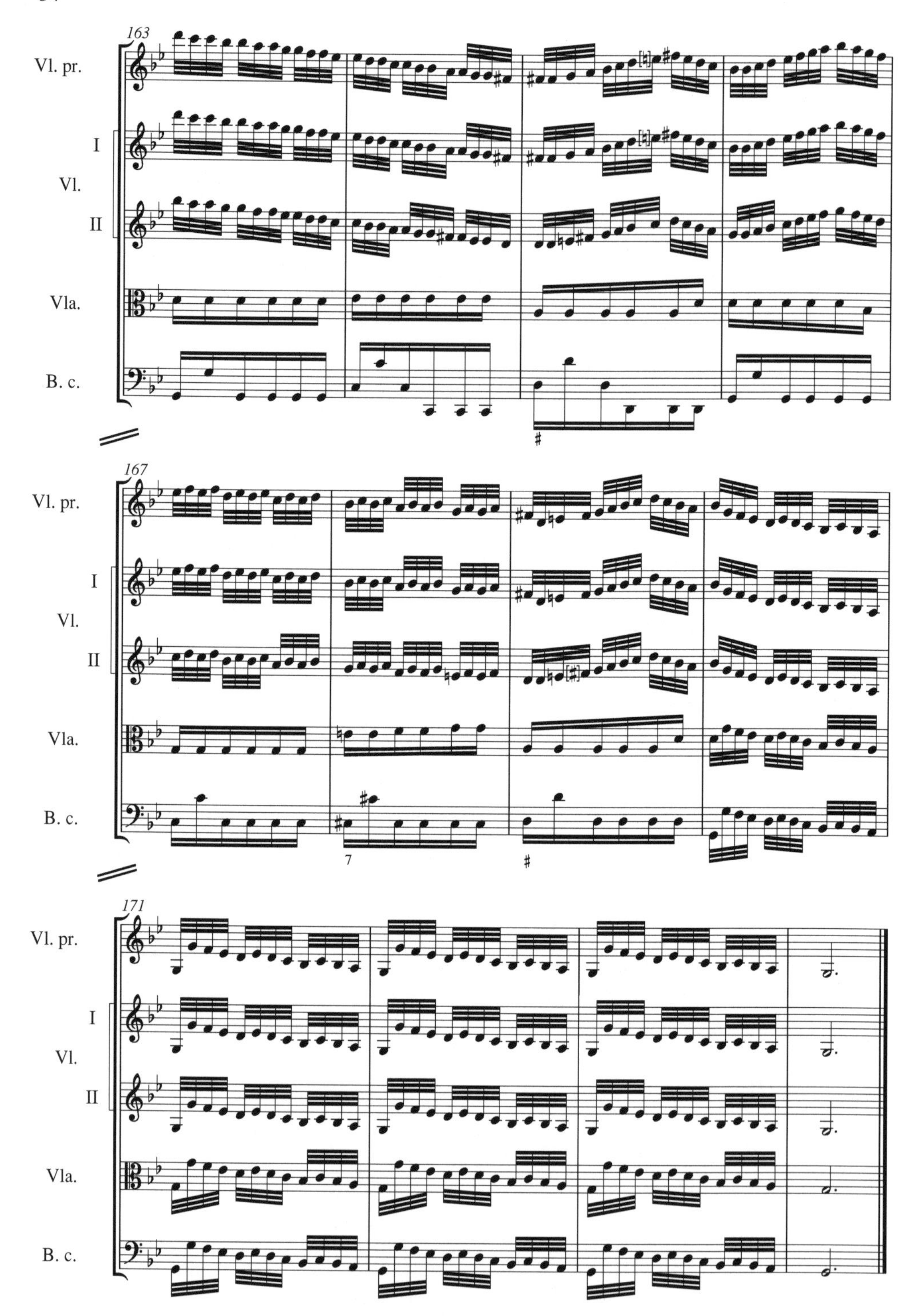
163
Vl. pr.
I
Vl.
II
Vla.
B. c.
167
Vl. pr.
I
Vl.
II
Vla.
B. c.
7
171
Vl. pr.
I
Vl.
II
Vla.
B. c.

II. Adagio

F Toglie alle membra lasse il suo riposo il timore de'lampi e tuoni fieri e de

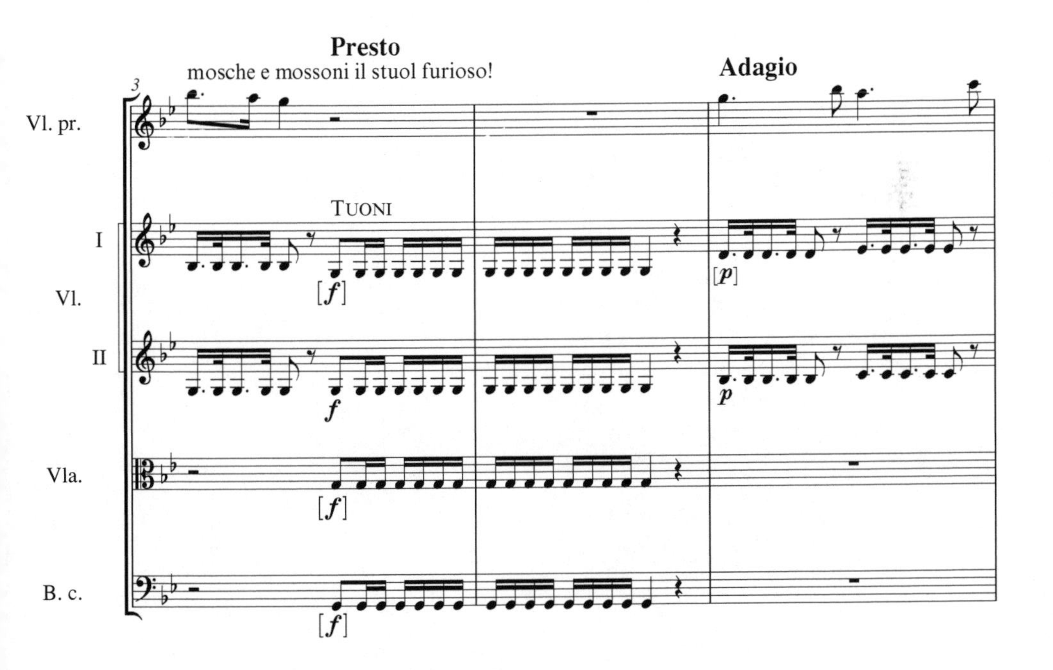

Presto
Vl. pr.
I
Vl.
II
Vla.
B. c.
Adagio
Vl. pr.
I
Vl.
II
Vla.
B. c.
Vl. pr.
I
Vl.
II

Presto
14
Vl. pr.
I
Vl.
II
Vla.
B. c.
[f]
f
17
Adagio
[p]
p
20
Presto
Adagio

III. Presto

TEMPO IMPETTUOSO D'ESTATE

G Ah che pur troppo i suoi timor son veri, tuona e fulmina il ciel e grandi-

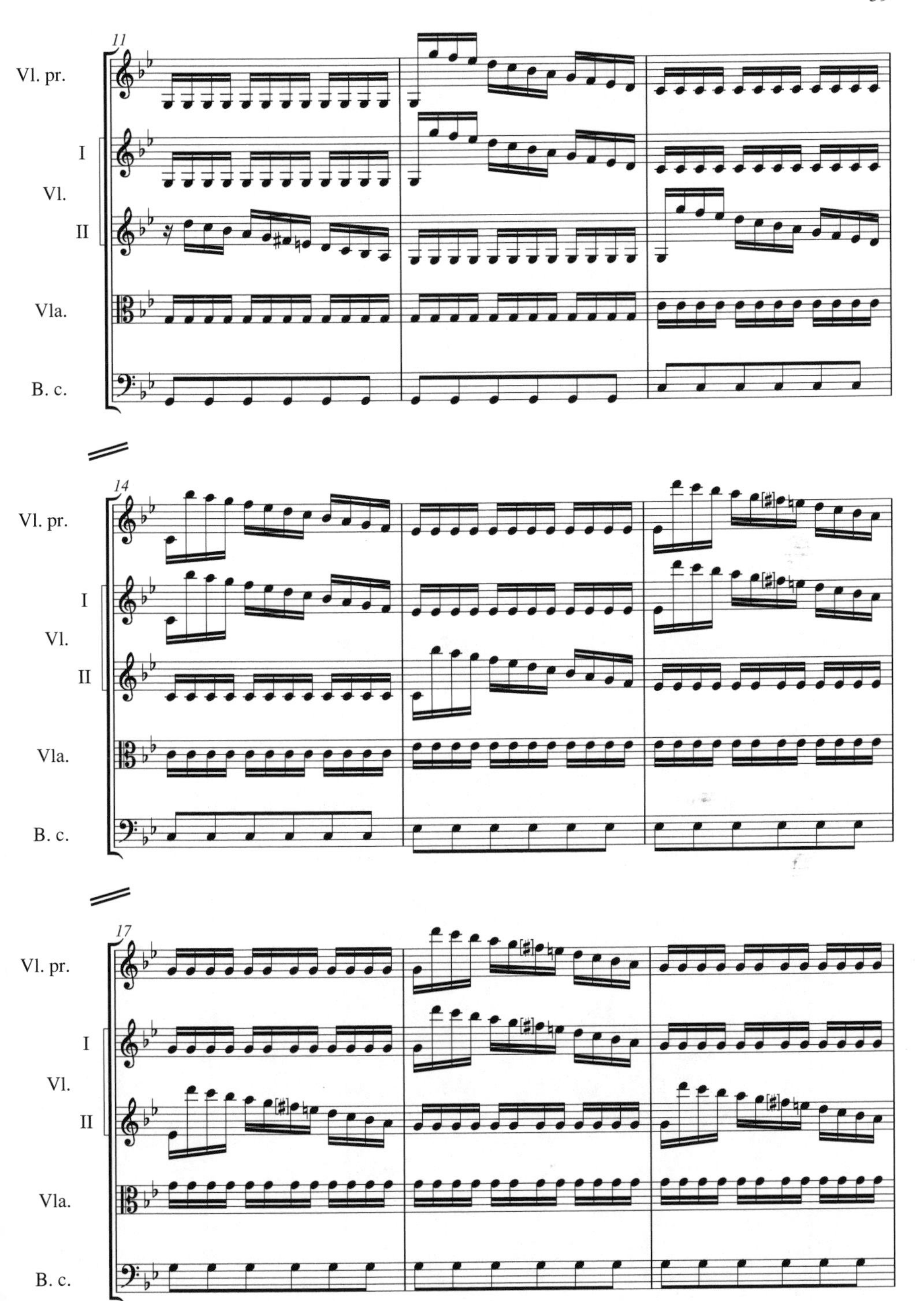
11
Vl. pr.
I
Vl.
II
Vla.
B. c.
14
Vl. pr.
I
Vl.
II
Vla.
B. c.
17
Vl. pr.
I
Vl.
II
Vla.
B. c.

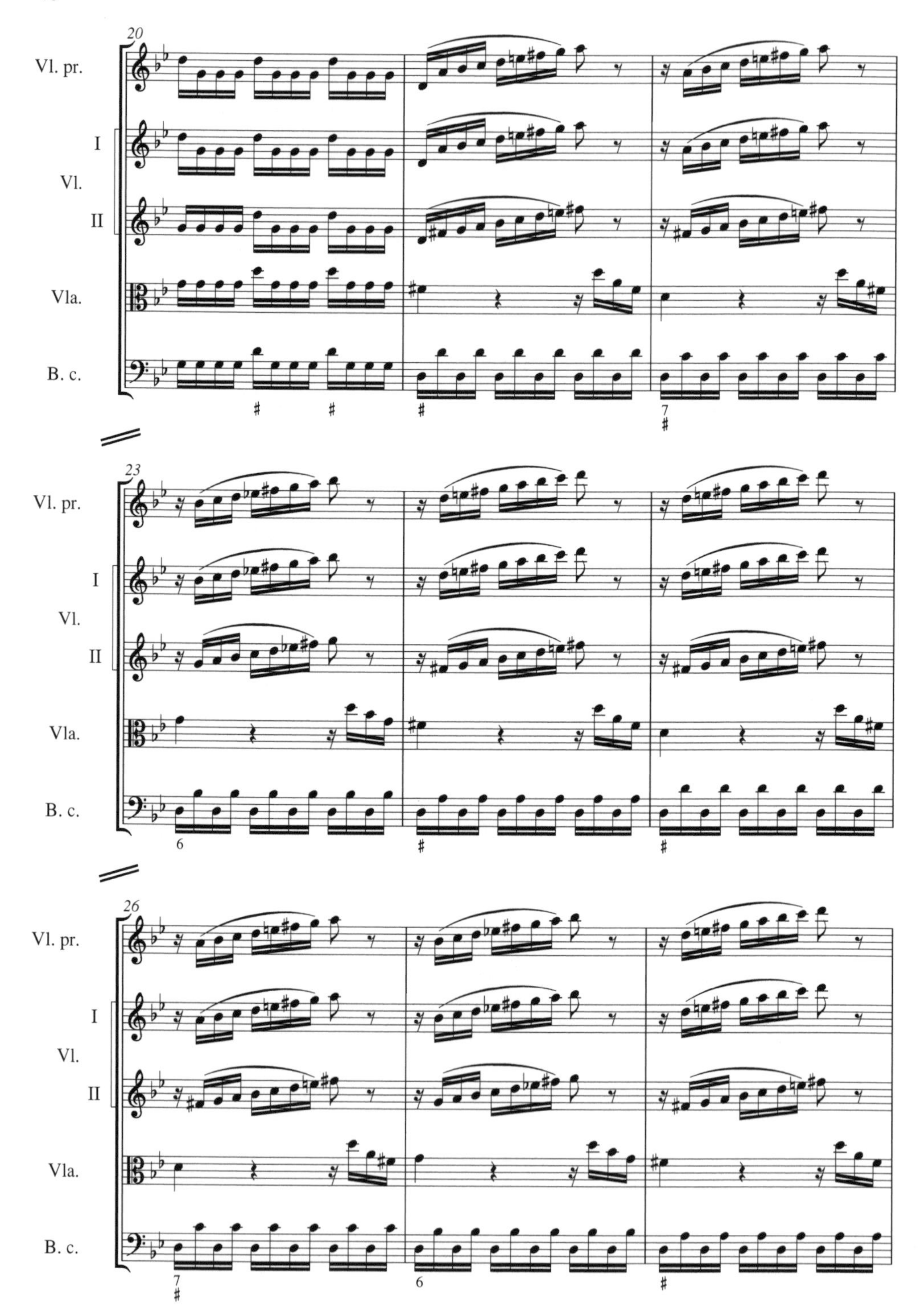
20
Vl. pr.
I
Vl.
II
Vla.
B. c.
23
Vl. pr.
I
Vl.
II
Vla.
B. c.
26
Vl. pr.
I
Vl.
II
Vla.
B. c.

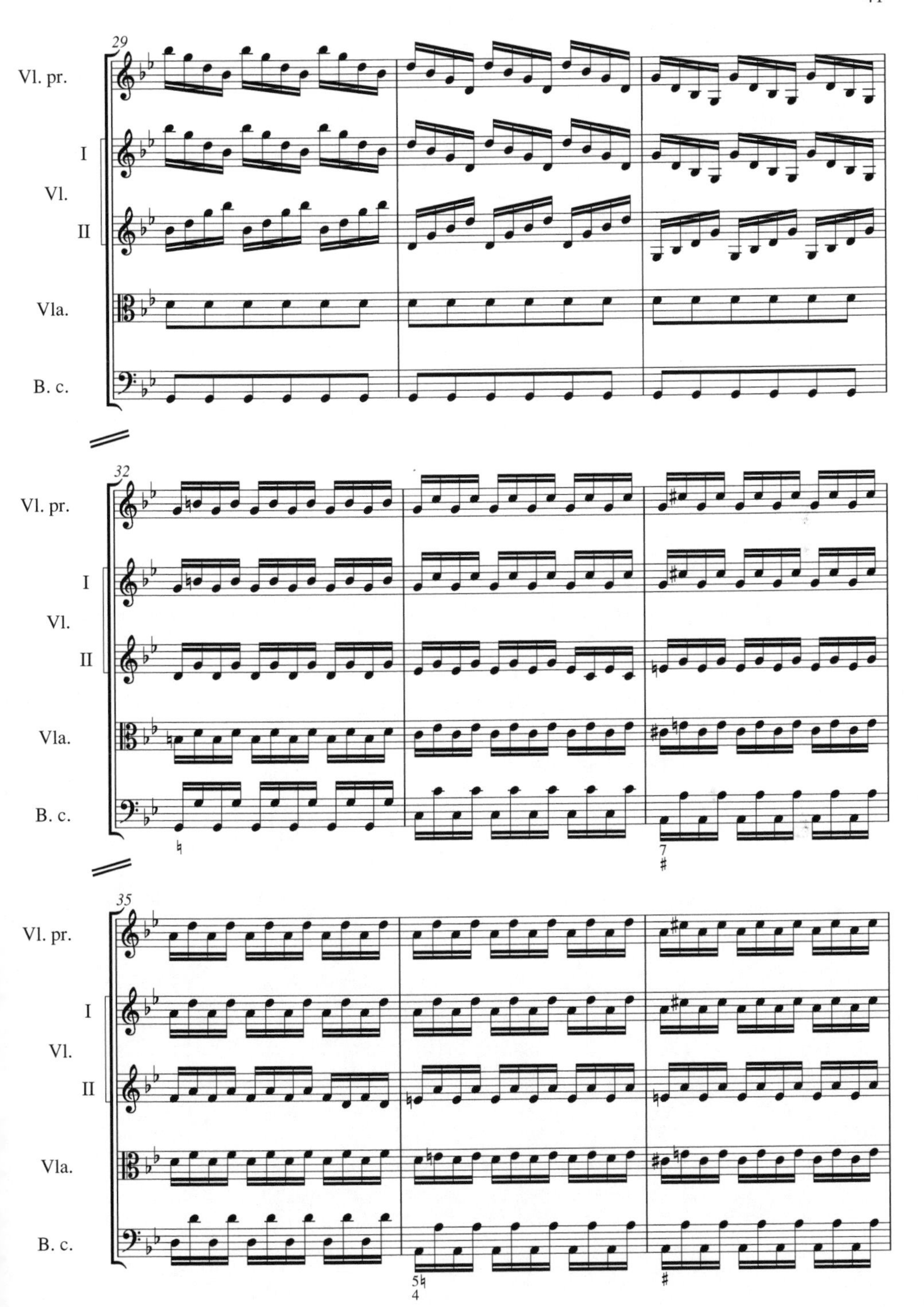
29
Vl. pr.
I
Vl.
II
Vla.
B. c.
32
Vl. pr.
I
Vl.
II
Vla.
B. c.
35
Vl. pr.
I
Vl.
II
Vla.
B. c.

38
Solo
Vl. pr.
I
Vl.
II
Vla.
B. c.
41
Vl. pr.
I
Vl.
II
Vla.
p
p
p
44
Vl. pr.
I
Vl.
II
Vla.
p
[p]
[p]

*) = sul D, G

59
Vl. pr.
I
Vl.
II
Vla.
B. c.
7
7
62
Vl. pr.
I
Vl.
II
Vla.
B. c.
6
7
♮
65
Vl. pr.
I
Vl.
II
Vla.
B. c.

68
Vl. pr.
I
Vl.
II
Vla.
B. c.
6
5
♭
5
4
♮
71
74
Solo
[sim.]
77
80

83
Vl. pr.
I
Vl.
II
Vla.
B. c.
Tutti
86
Vl. pr.
I
Vl.
II
Vla.
B. c.
7
89
Vl. pr.
I
Vl.
II
Vla.
B. c.
7
7

92
Vl. pr.
I
Vl.
II
Vla.
B. c.
7
95
Solo
Tasto solo
98
101
Tutti
[Tutti]

104
Vl. pr.
I
Vl.
II
Vla.
B. c.
107
Solo
[p]
p
p
[p]
110

Tutti
113
Vl. pr.
[f]
I
Vl.
[f]
II
f
Vla.
[f]
B. c.
5
3
[f]
116
Solo
Vl. pr.
I
Vl.
II
Vla.
B. c.
119
Tutti
Vl. pr.
I
Vl.
II
Vla.
B. c.

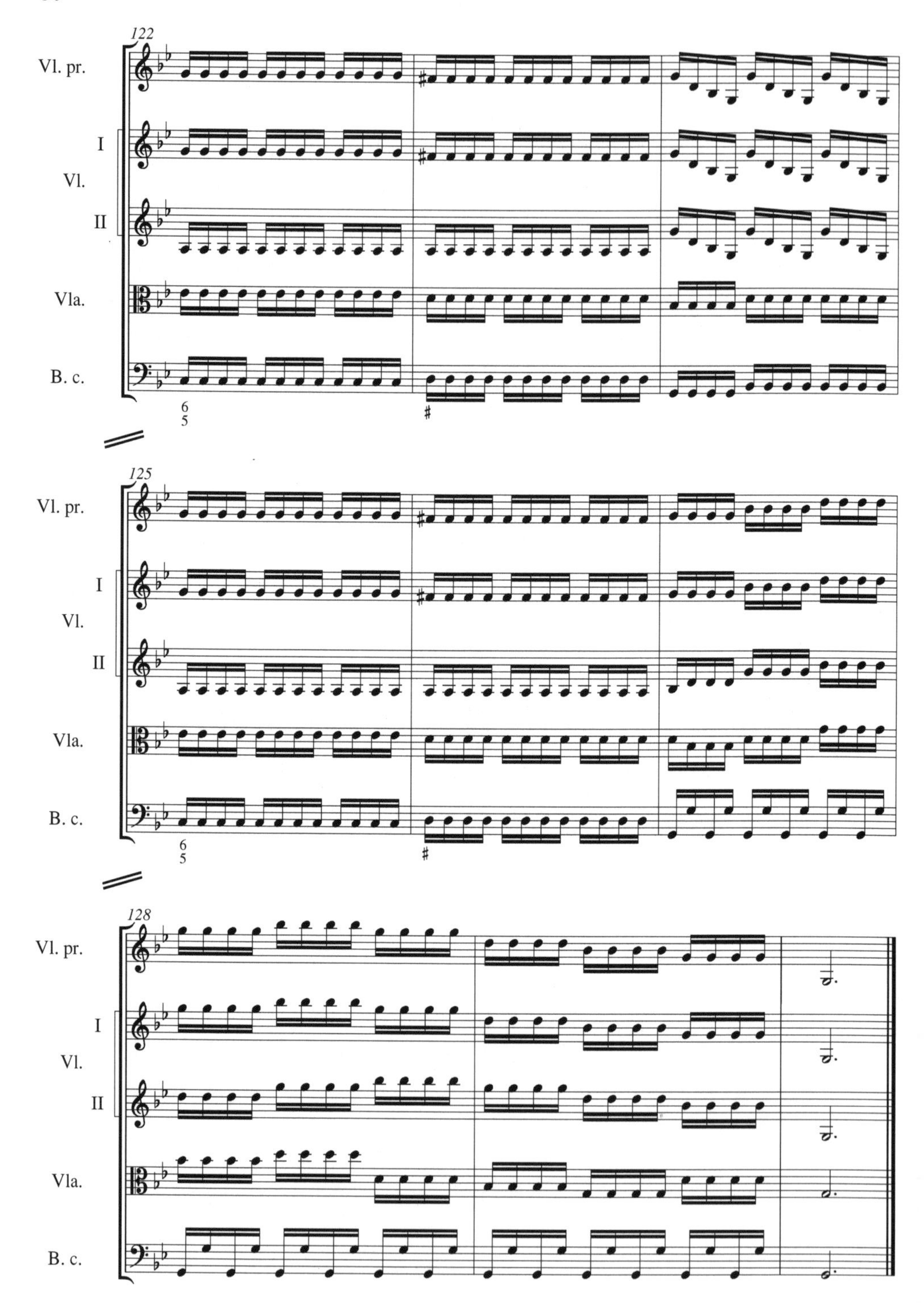
122
Vl. pr.
I
Vl.
II
Vla.
B. c.
6
5
♯
125
Vl. pr.
I
Vl.
II
Vla.
B. c.
6
5
♯
128
Vl. pr.
I
Vl.
II
Vla.
B. c.

CONCERTO No. 3 L'AUTUNNO

Antonio Vivaldi
(1678–1741)
Op. 8/3
RV 293

I. **Allegro**

BALLO E CANTO DE' VILLANELLI

A Celebra il vilanel con balli e canti del felice raccolto il bel piacere

Edited by Simon Launchbury

Vl. pr.
I
Vl.
II
Vla.
B. c.
[p]
p
Solo
f
[f]
[p]
p

Tutti
Vl. pr.
I
Vl.
II
Vla.
B. c.
L'UBRIACO
B e del liquor di Bacco accesi tanti
Solo
UBRIACHI

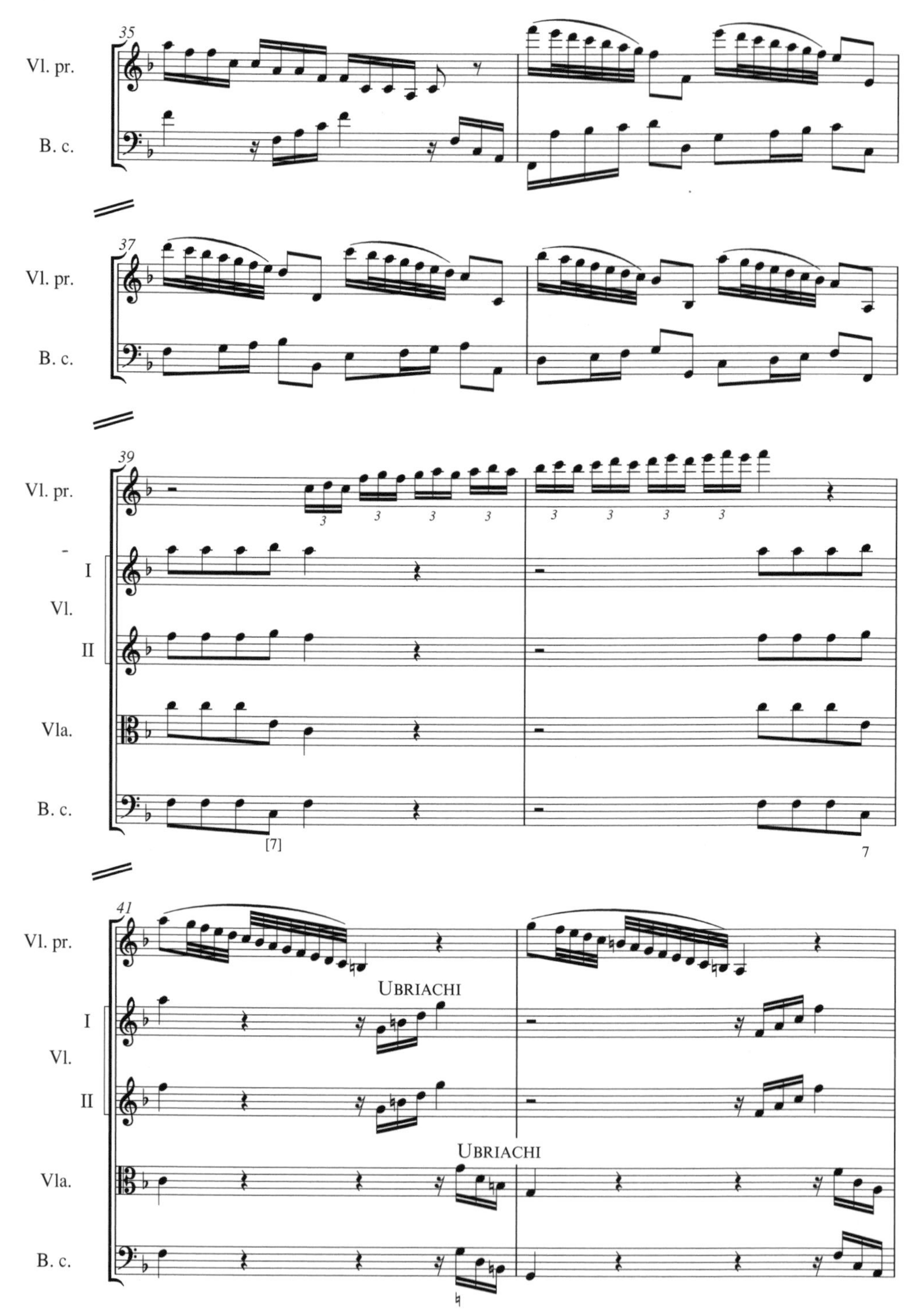

35
Vl. pr.
B. c.
37
Vl. pr.
B. c.
39
Vl. pr.
I
Vl.
II
Vla.
B. c.
[7]
7
41
Vl. pr.
UBRIACHI
I
Vl.
II
UBRIACHI
Vla.
B. c.

43
Vl. pr.
I
Vl.
II
Vla.
B. c.
46
Vl. pr.
I
Vl.
II
Vla.
B. c.
49
Vl. pr.
I
Vl.
II
Vla.
B. c.

Vl. pr.
I
Vl.
II
Vla.
B. c.
Tutti

60
Vl. pr.
I
Vl.
II
Vla.
B. c.
7 7 7♭ 7 ♯ 7 ♯ 7
UBRIACO
Solo
64
p
[p]
[p]
p
[p]
68
p
[p]
6

71
Vl. pr.
B. c.
74
Vl. pr.
B. c.
77
Tutti
Vl. pr.
I
Vl.
II
Vla.
B. c.
81
Vl. pr.
I
Vl.
II
Vla.
B. c.

84
Vl. pr.
I
Vl.
II
Vla.
B. c.
7♭
7
♮
87
Vl. pr.
I
Vl.
II
Vla.
B. c.
Larghetto
L'UBRIACO CHE DORME
C finiscono col sonno il lor godere.
89
Vl. pr.
p
I
Vl.
II
B. c.

93
Vl. pr.
più p
I
più p
Vl.
II
[più p]
97
Vl. pr.
pp
I
pp
Vl.
II
pp
Vla.
pp
101
Vl. pr.
I
Vl.
II
Vla.

Allegro assai
104
Vl. pr.
I
Vl.
II
Vla.
B. c.
[f]
f
108
112

II. Adagio molto

UBRIACHI DORMIENTI

D fà ch'ogn'uno tralasci e balli e canti l'aria che temperata dà piacere, e la

22
Vl. pr.
I
Vl.
II
Vla.
B. c.
30
p
più p
38
pp

III. Allegro

LA CACCIA

E I cacciator alla nov'alba à caccia con corni, schioppi, e canni escono fuore

16
Vl. pr.
I
Vl.
II
Vla.
B. c.
7
7
7
23
Solo
31

38
Vl. pr.
Tutti
I
Vl.
II
Vla.
B. c.
45
Solo
52

[sim.]
Vl. pr.
B. c.
Tutti
I
Vl.
II
Vla.
La fiera che fugge
F fugge la belva, e seguono la traccia;

G già sbigottita, e lassa al gran
79
[sim.]
Vl. pr.
I
Vl.
II
Vla.
B. c.
84
rumore de'schioppi e canni, ferita minaccia
88

92
Vl. pr.
I
Vl.
II
Vla.
B. c.
95
Tutti
100
Solo

106
Vl. pr.
I
Vl.
II
Vla.
B. c.
111
Tutti
116

123
Vl. pr.
I
Vl.
II
Vla.
B. c.
La fiera fuggendo muore
H languida di fuggir, mà oppressa muore.
127
131

135
Vl. pr.
I
Vl.
II
Vla.
Tasto solo
B. c.
141
tr
[Tutti]
7
7
149

CONCERTO No. 4 L'INVERNO

Antonio Vivaldi
(1678–1741)
Op. 8/4
RV 297

I. Allegro non molto

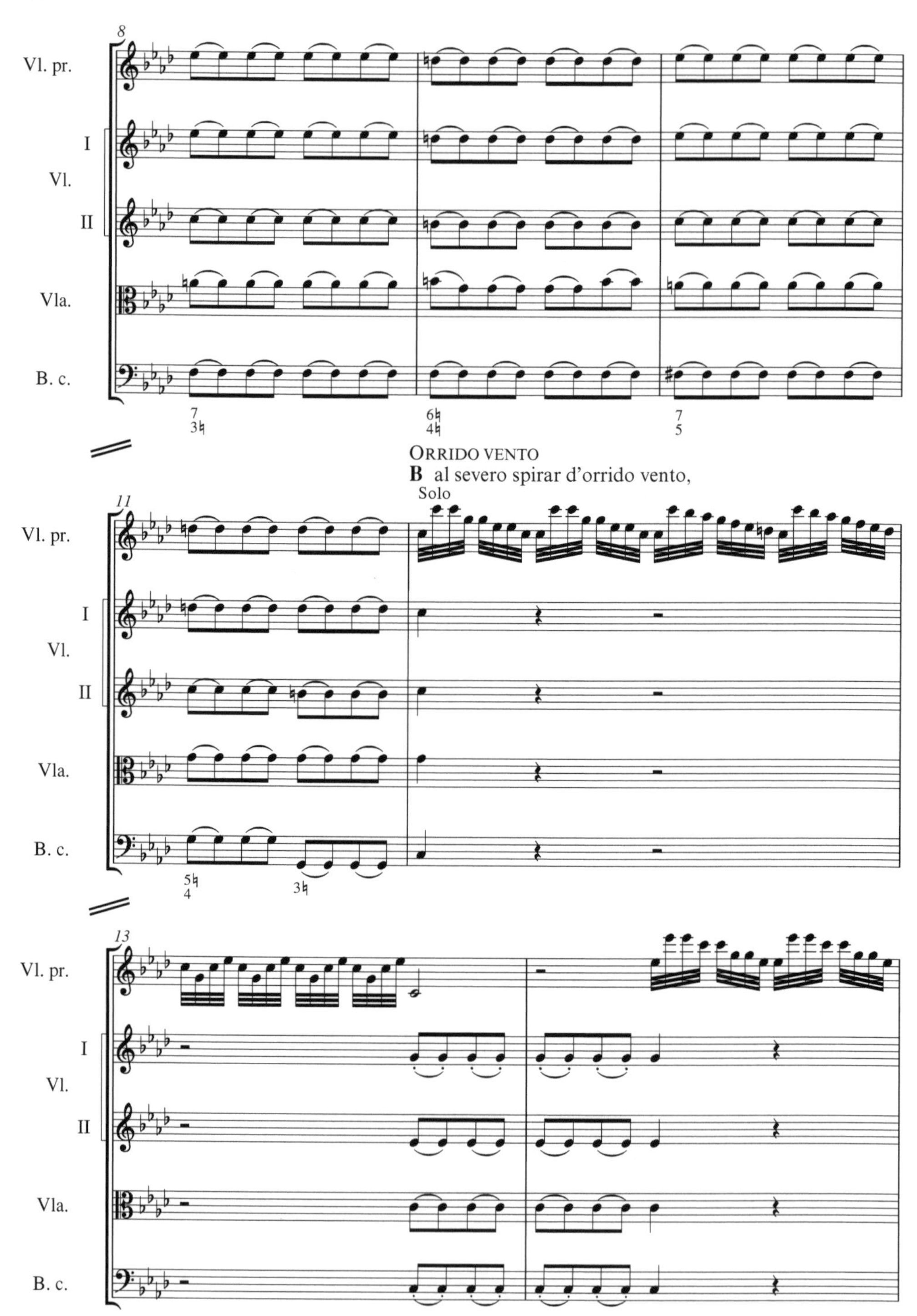
Vl. pr.
I
Vl.
II
Vla.
B. c.
ORRIDO VENTO
B al severo spirar d'orrido vento,
Solo

15
Vl. pr.
I
Vl.
II
Vla.
B. c.
17
Vl. pr.
I
Vl.
II
Vla.
B. c.
18
Vl. pr.
Tutti
I
[sim.]
Vl.
II
Vla.
B. c.
4
2♭

CORRERE, E BATTER LI
C correr battendo i

21

[*sim.*]

Vl. pr.

I

Vl.

II

Vla.

B. c.

6
4♮

6♮
3

♮

PIEDI PER IL FREDDO
piedi ogni momento;

23

Vl. pr.

I

Vl.

II

Vla.

B. c.

27
Vl. pr.
B. c.
28
Vl. pr.
B. c.
29
Vl. pr.
B. c.
30
Vl. pr.
B. c.
31
Vl. pr.
B. c.
7
6
7
6

32
Vl. pr.
B. c.
7
♮
33
Vl. pr.
VENTI
I
Vl.
II
Vla.
B. c.
34
Vl. pr.
I
Vl.
II
Vla.
B. c.
7
3♮

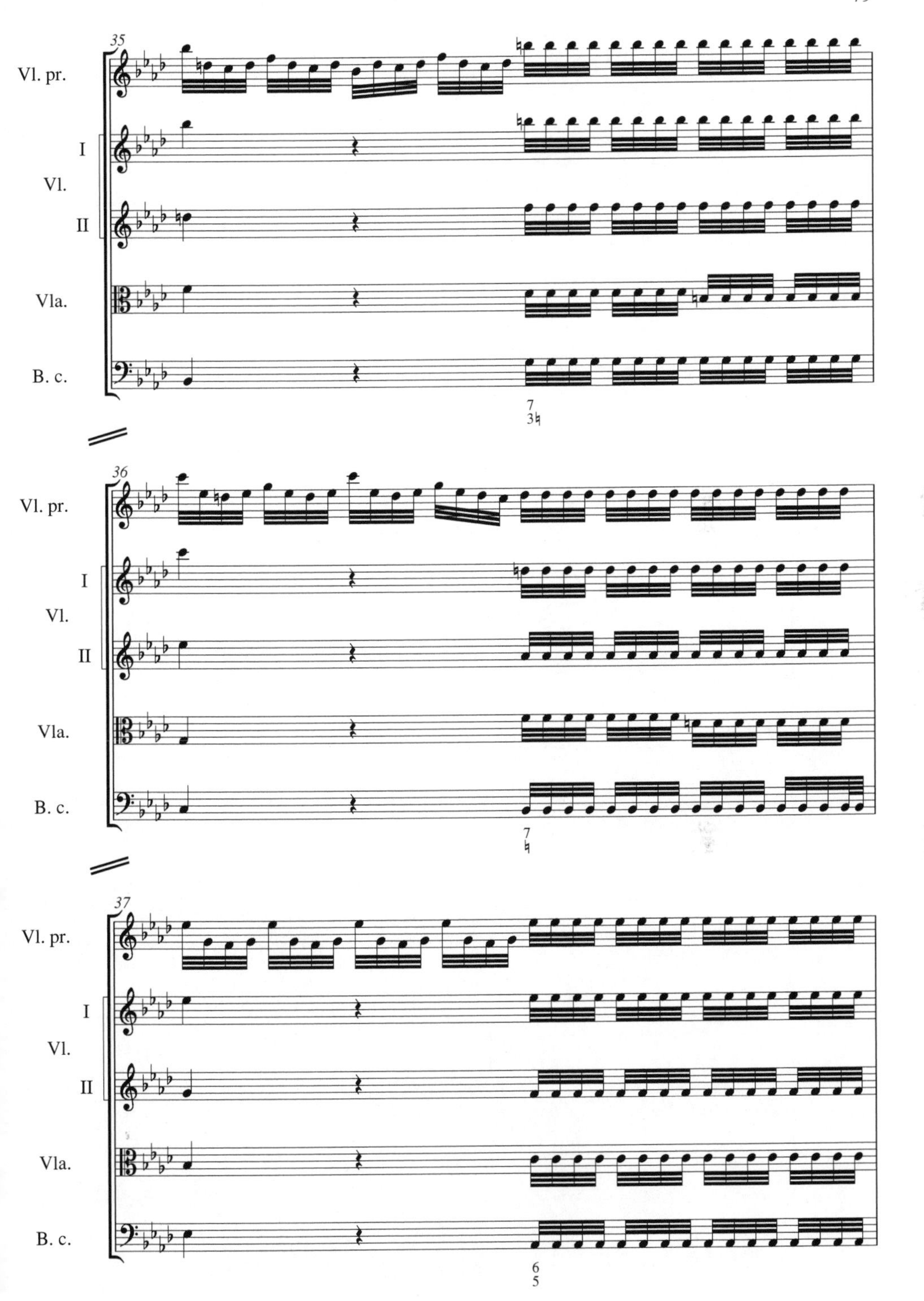
35
Vl. pr.
I
Vl.
II
Vla.
B. c.
7
3♮
36
Vl. pr.
I
Vl.
II
Vla.
B. c.
7
♮
37
Vl. pr.
I
Vl.
II
Vla.
B. c.
6
5

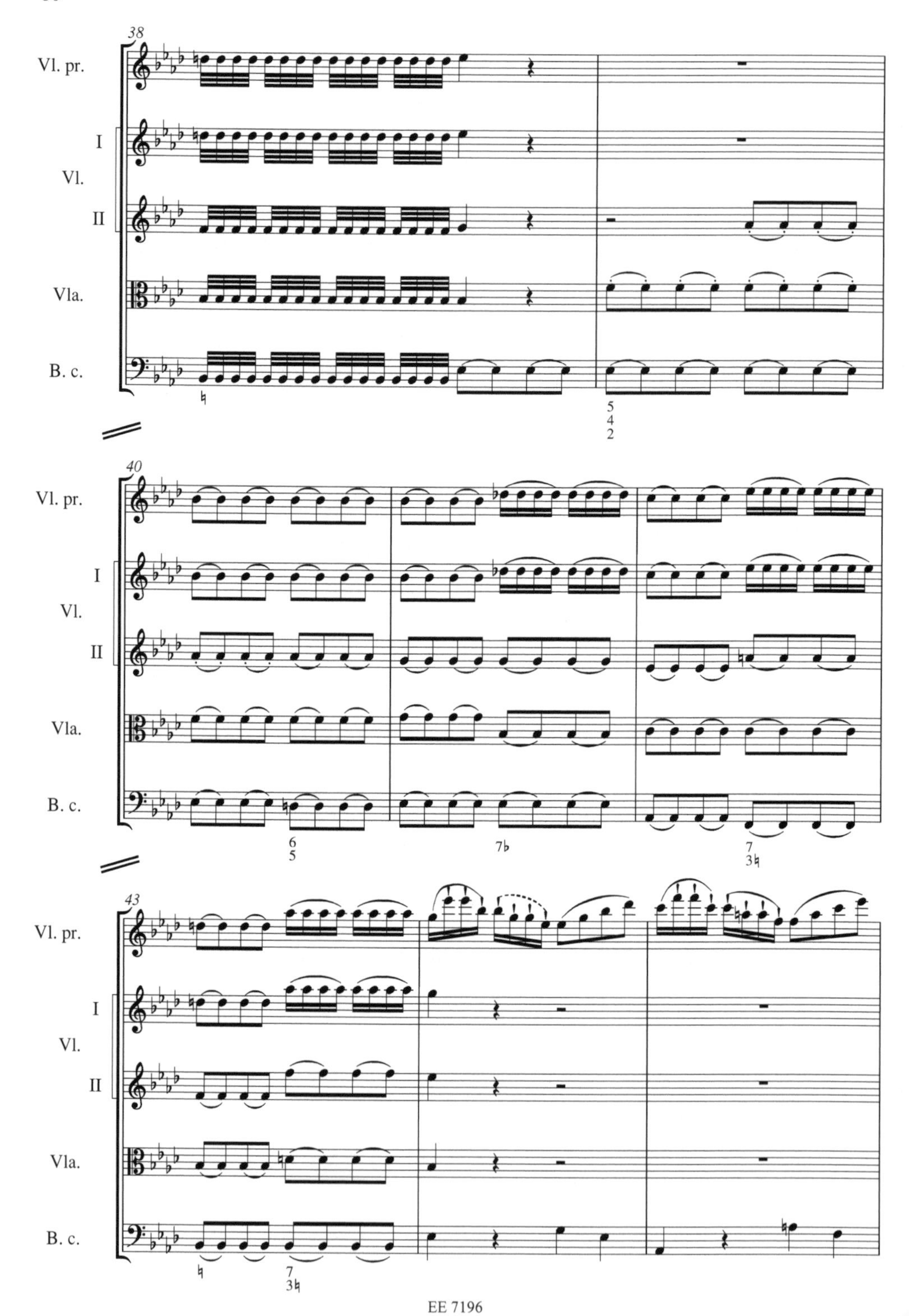
38
Vl. pr.
I
Vl.
II
Vla.
B. c.
40
Vl. pr.
I
Vl.
II
Vla.
B. c.
43
Vl. pr.
I
Vl.
II
Vla.
B. c.

BATTER LI DENTI
D e pel soverchio gel battere i denti;
46
Vl. pr.
I
Vl.
II
Vla.
p
B. c.
48
Vl. pr.
I
Vl.
II
Vla.
49
Vl. pr.
I
Vl.
II
Vla.

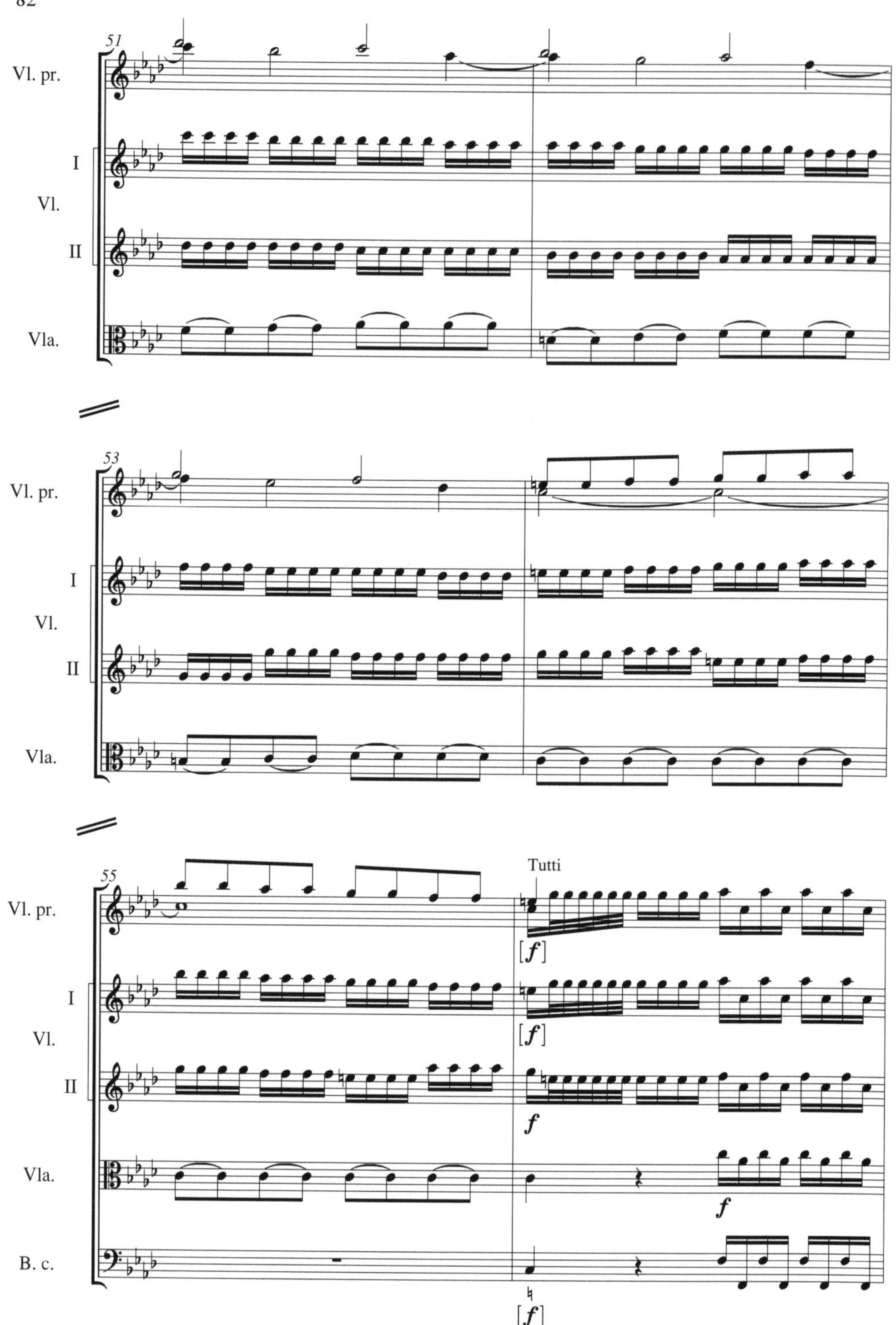
51
Vl. pr.
I
Vl.
II
Vla.
53
Vl. pr.
I
Vl.
II
Vla.
55
Tutti
Vl. pr.
[f]
I
[f]
Vl.
II
f
Vla.
f
B. c.
[f]

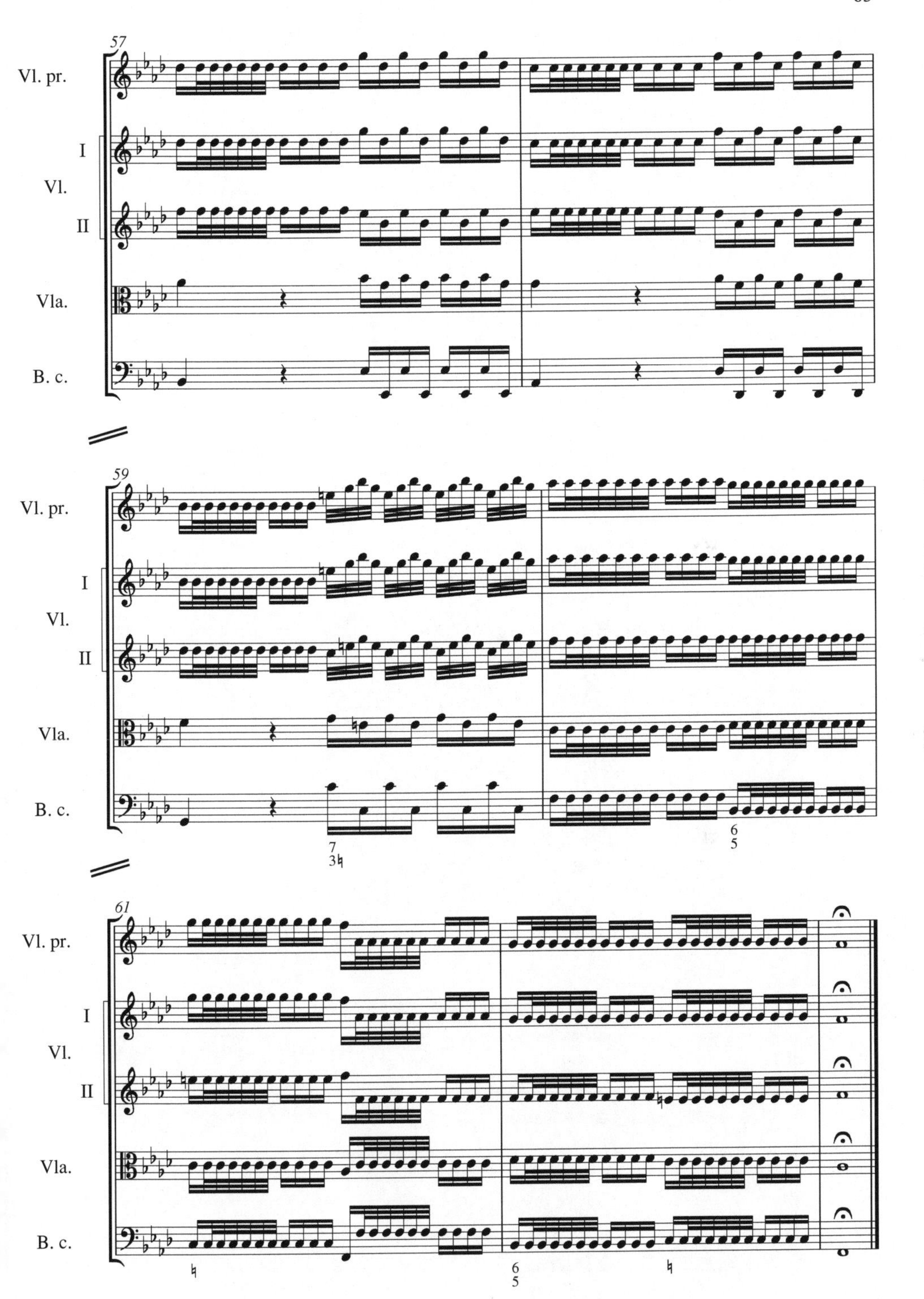
57
Vl. pr.
I
Vl.
II
Vla.
B. c.
59
Vl. pr.
I
Vl.
II
Vla.
B. c.
7
3♮
6
5
61
Vl. pr.
I
Vl.
II
Vla.
B. c.
♮
6
5
♮

II. Largo

E passar al fuoco i di quieti e contenti mentre la pioggia fuor bagna ben cento
Solo
Violino principale
[mf]
LA PIOGGIA
pizz.
I
Violino
f
pizz.
II
f
con l'arco
Viola
pp
Organo e Violoncello [Basso continuo]
sempre p
3
Vl. pr.
I
Vl.
II
Vla.
B. c.
6
Vl. pr.
tr
I
Vl.
II
Vla.
B. c.
5
4

9
Vl. pr.
I
Vl.
II
Vla.
B. c.
♮
7
5
4
3
7
12
Vl. pr.
I
Vl.
II
Vla.
B. c.
6
6
6
15
Vl. pr.
I
Vl.
II
Vla.
B. c.

III. Allegro
F caminar sopra il giaccio
Solo
Violino principale
I
Violino
II
Viola
Tasto solo
arcate lunghe
Organo e Violoncello [Basso continuo]
6
Vl. pr.
B. c.
12
Vl. pr.
B. c.
19
Vl. pr.
I
Vl.
II
Vla.
Tasto solo
B. c.

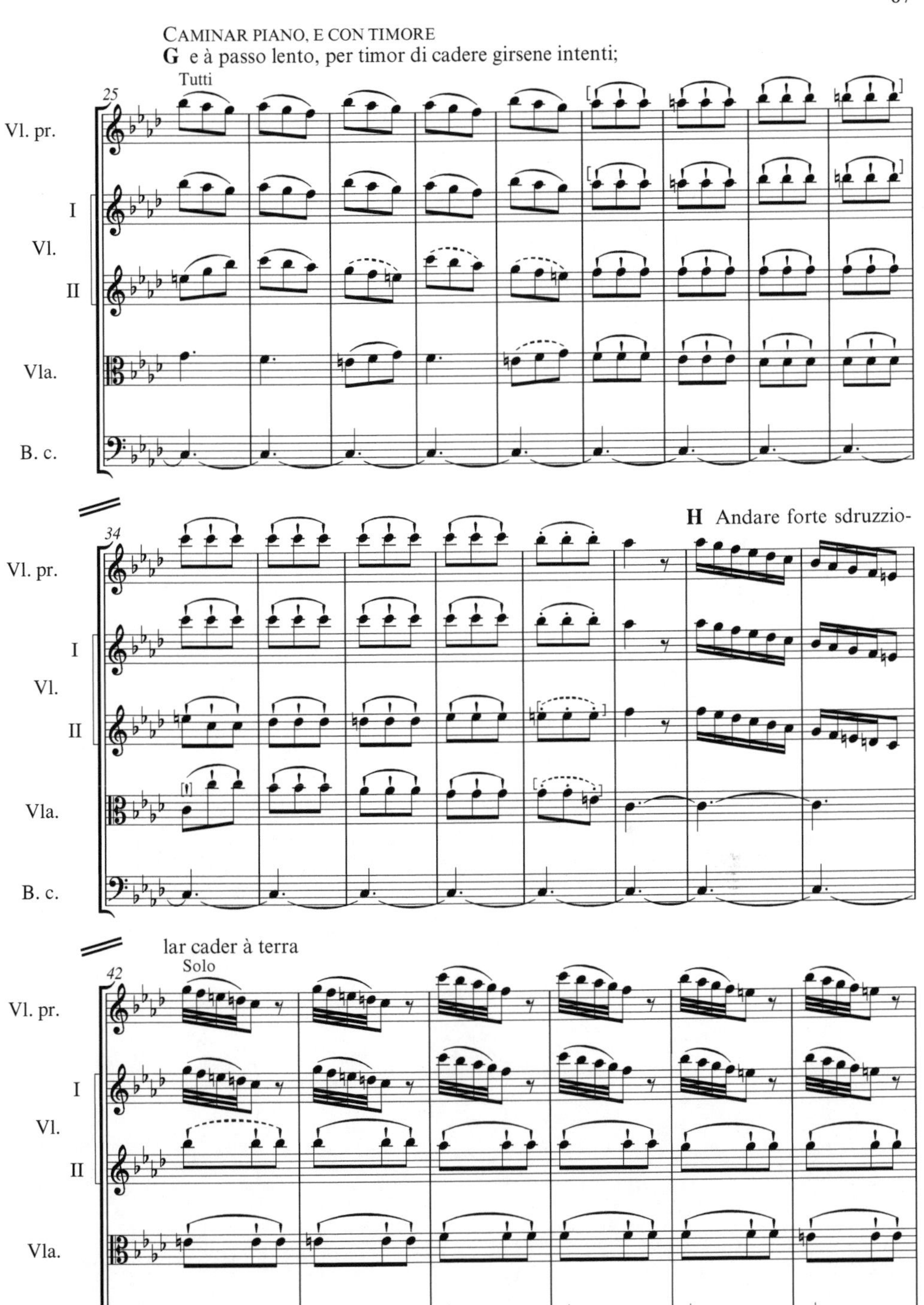
CAMINAR PIANO, E CON TIMORE
G e à passo lento, per timor di cadere girsene intenti;
Tutti
25
Vl. pr.
I
Vl.
II
Vla.
B. c.
34
H Andare forte sdruzzio-
lar cader à terra
Solo
42

CADER A TERRA
CORRER FORTE
I di nuovo ir sopra'l giaccio e correr forte
48
Tutti
Solo
[sim.]
Vl. pr.
I
Vl.
II
Vla.
Tutti
B. c.
55
p
p
Tasto solo
62

68
Vl. pr.
I
Vl.
II
Vla.
Tasto solo
B. c.
74
79

Tutti
Vl. pr.
I
Vl.
II
Vla.
B. c.
L sin ch'il giaccio si rompe, e si disserra;
Solo
Lento
Il vento sirocco
M sentir uscir dalle ferrate porte

109
Vl. pr.
I
Vl.
II
Vla.
115
Vl. pr.
I
Vl.
II
Vla.
[a tempo]
IL VENTO BOREA E TUTTI LI VENTI
N Sirocco, Borea, e tutti i venti in guerra.
120
Solo
Vl. pr.
I
Vl.
II
Vla.
B. c.

123
Vl. pr.
I
Vl.
II
Vla.
[Tutti]
B. c.
125
Vl. pr.
I
Vl.
II
Vla.
B. c.
127
Vl. pr.
I
Vl.
II
Vla.
B. c.

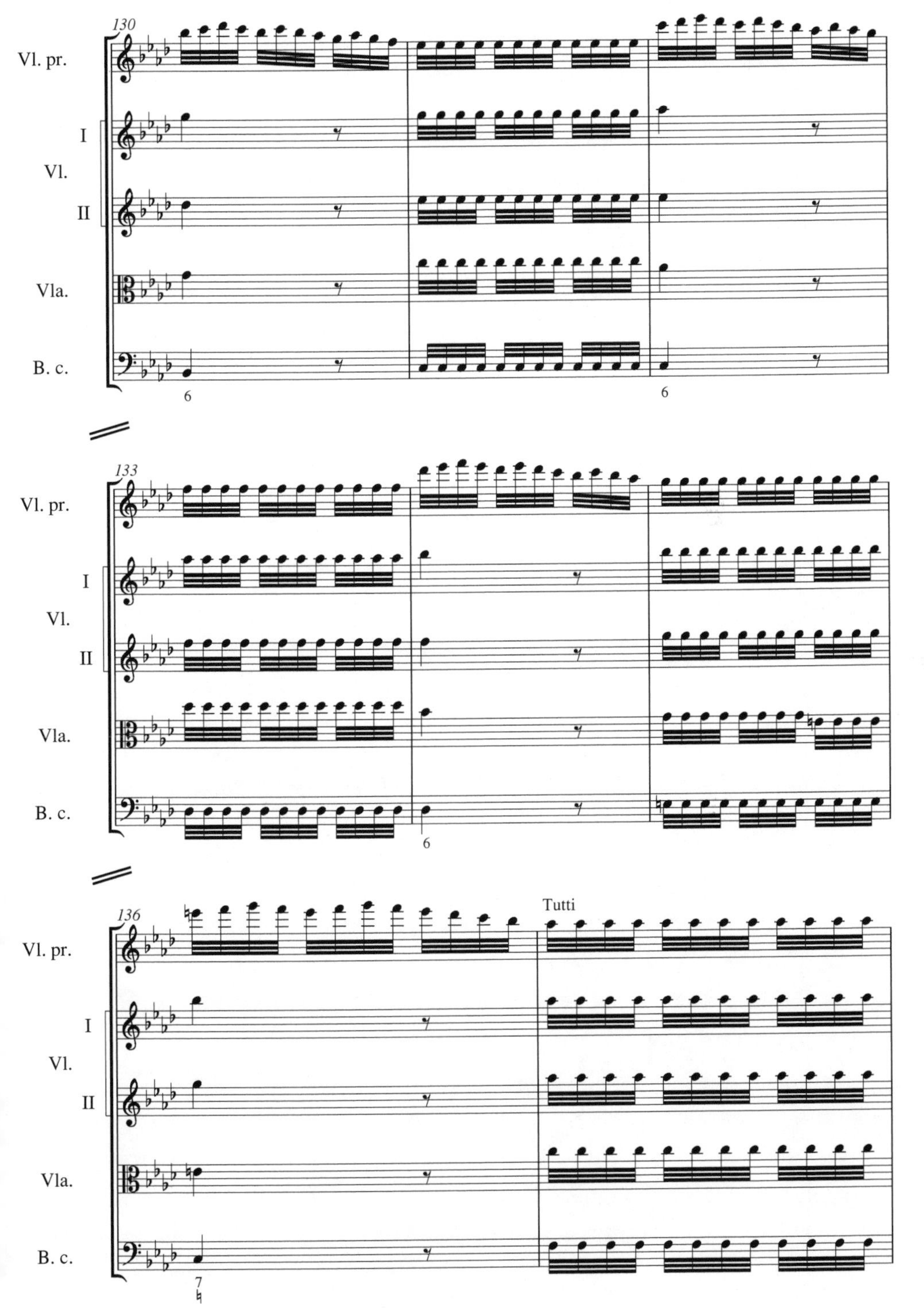
130
Vl. pr.
I
Vl.
II
Vla.
B. c.
6
6
133
Vl. pr.
I
Vl.
II
Vla.
B. c.
6
136
Tutti
Vl. pr.
I
Vl.
II
Vla.
B. c.
7

138
Vl. pr.
I
Vl.
II
Vla.
B. c.
140
Vl. pr.
I
Vl.
II
Vla.
B. c.
143
Vl. pr.
I
Vl.
II
Vla.
B. c.
5
4

146
Vl. pr.
I
Vl.
II
Vla.
B. c.
148
Vl. pr.
I
Vl.
II
Vla.
B. c.
Quest'è'l verno, mà tal, che gioja apporte.
151
Vl. pr.
I
Vl.
II
Vla.
B. c.
5
4